THREE GLASGOW WRITERS

Three Glasgow Writers

A collection of writing by

Alex.Hamilton
James Kelman
Tom Leonard

Published by The Molendinar Press

The Molendinar Press
73 Robertson Street
Glasgow G2

This edition first published 1976
© Alex. Hamilton, James Kelman & Tom Leonard
ISBN 0 904002 13 6

Published with the assistance of the Scottish Arts Council

Made and printed in Great Britain By Salesbury Press Ltd.,
Llandybie, Wales

ALEX HAMILTON

TOM LEONARD

JAMES KELMAN

My first two stories in this collection are part of a sequence written for Glasgow children. For a short period I taught English in a Glasgow comprehensive and it became clear that, no matter how "good" or "interesting" literature might appear to be to the teacher, many of the pupils were antagonistic to it.

In a short introduction it is not possible to give the reasons for this in any great detail, but if, in the Television Age, writing is going to compete and prove its effectiveness as an art form and news-bringer, it has to be of immediate interest to a possible young audience.

'Gallus, did you say?' and 'Our Merry' have tried to capture areas which interest young adults, and to present these in such a way that the audience's enthusiasm is immediately aroused. They are set in a locale in which I grew up myself, and which is shared by the vast majority of Glasgow children — the post-war housing scheme with few facilities, set in an anonymous complex of streets.

The attempt at faithful transcription of dialect needs, I think, no explanation. If a teacher, say, wishes to use these stories with a class, there is sufficient controversy, linguistic as well as political and economic, to stimulate discussion — after the initial cracking of the code, which is a conscious linguistic device in itself.

The third story 'Birthday' was inspired by the legend of Philoctetes and the Bow.

Alex. Hamilton

Gallus, did you say?

I was frightened, there's no getting away from that. Just as frightened as the rest of them were; but at least I had the excuse. I'm not trying to get out of it or anything, but I did have to go home and watch Maureen. That's my wee sister, by the way. My da was working late every Wednesday at that time, and my mother's a telephone operator so she's always out from teatime till half past ten. Anyway, that's not to say I'd have helped out even if I could have, because that lot are a real rough crowd to have anything to do with, so you couldn't really blame Tommy and them for not going. Though it was his ball that caused it, mind you

Still, the fact that I got the story from Big Mikey who's their kind of leader just makes Wullie's part in it all the more as if you couldn't believe it. Pure gallus, it must have been.

What happened was this.

It was in the school holidays, and you know what that's like. You begin to get a bit fed up near the end because your ma's always shouting at you for being round her feet all day, and I suppose you are, right enough. But you know what I mean? She's that edgy, and so's everbody else's, and I suppose it's something to do with having all that freedom for six or seven weeks, that you start to feel that holidays are all right, but they're maybe not just as great as they were when they started? Course, the last thing you'd ever let onto the boys is that you're bored or that, and you wish school had started up again.

But that was what was happening, though. I mean, we'd all got that cheesed off going up the public where we just got chased by the parkies for playing with the ball on their wee bit precious grass — I mean, what's it for, but? you just opposed to look at it and say how nice it is and that? We got yon way we'd started just going round to the wee school, and the jannie used to let us play on the pitch as long as we didn't leave anything lying about when we'd finished the game.

(Actually, my da says he had to let us in and he got paid overtime for just checking a bunch of boys and doing hee-haw besides, and that's easy money when you're the size he is. He used to give us a game if he was feeling friendly as well. Da says he should be quite good and all, nothing else to do, and getting paid time and a half for kicking a ball about.)

Anyway, it was a great night, nice and warm, so we took our jackets and jerseys off for the goals, and started off playing three a side till the rest came out from their teas to make it up to a big game.

We were getting on fine; I was playing with Tommy because it was his ball and he likes me in goals, and wee Joe was on our side as well. Wullie was on the other team, and he was playing along with Davey and Davey's cousin that sometimes comes over for the day because he doesn't live all that far. So that was the line-up, and nothing much happening. You know how it is, you just mess about, don't use up your energy or that till you get to maybe six or seven a side, because if you do, soon as the others come in and you start to get a big decent couple of teams on the go, the new lot think you're duff because you're half done in. Know what I mean? no stamina left.

Quite good anyway. You can always get a laugh at Tommy, because even when he's playing hard and for real, he's still a bampot. Gawky, you know? My ma says he'll be a fine big boy when he grows up, because his father's a police and his mother's big and all, but I'll wait till I see it. He's just legs the now as far as I'm concerned, and the rest of the boys and all, and you can get a good laugh at him just looking.

"Moan," he says, "Chip it ower. Fur thi heid."

And somebody does, just for a laugh because it's not a serious game or that, and sure as fate up he goes. I'm not kidding you — but maybe you've got a mate like that as well? you see quite a lot of them hanging about like big Tommy. Up he goes, like as if he's the Wee Man or somebody, and you can see he's concentrating, on his face, the way his tongue curls away round about his earhole, up like a gawky rocket gone wrong off the launching pad. One leg this way, the other somewhere else, and his hands and head down somewhere round about Australia. You've got to give Tommy about a mile and a half clearance when he's diving after a shot, though that can be good if he's on your side. No, I mean it — I've seen other teams' goalies doubled up in kinks when he comes charging in at them, one foot falling over the other. But it's great, because they're that helpless with laughter that they can't stop the ball going past them into the net — or between the jerseys I should say. Right laugh it is.

Then you should see him. That overjoyed he is, flings his arms and legs about like a great pregnant hare or something, and you're opposed to go up and congratulate him on his skill and coordination and that. Fat chance. Liable to get your head knocked off with one of they great uncontrolled plates of meat swinging about.

Anyway, that was about the size ot it, just enjoying ourselves and having a wee laugh, when Wullie shouts out:

"Heh, look oot boays, here's trubbil cumin."

Well, when one of our boys shouts about trouble, it can be quite a few things. You know, it could be the jannie deciding to come it because he's been on the bevvy and doesn't like anybody that day; or it could be somebody's wee busybody sister out looking for him to try and break up the game, telling you that your ma wants you to go and get something at the shops when she could go quite as well, not having anything better to do but play at dolls and things. Pure jealousy, it is. Just because you know how to have a good time and they don't.

It wasn't either of they two things though, not this time.

"Whit izit, Wullie?" I says.

"Orr therr," he goes, "cumin up thi Circus."

Big Tommy comes prancing over, dribbling his feet in mistake for the ball, full of himself because he's just put one past Davey's cousin who was tying his lace at the time, and had shouted Keys anyway.

"Ach," he says, "thir awright that mob. Big Mikey an Cumpni, intit? Ah mean, fyi lee theym alane they doan't boathir aboot you. Eniwey, thiv goat a baw a thir ain."

Right enough, so they did, and they were passing it up and down to one another as they came along the Circus, and they looked quite quiet. Just like anybody else, you know?

"Cumoan," I says, "Tam's right. Fwi jiss get oan wi it thill no boathir us. Ah mean, thid oanlie want a gemm wi thi likes a us if wi wir thi oanlie wans wi thi baw, widint they?"

"Eniwey," says Davey, "therrz thi jannie hingin aboot sunnin izsel. Thill no try enihin oan if he's aboot."

Neither they did either. They came in and went straight over to the other pitch, never even a nod or a hullo to let you know you were still in your puff. Still, we all thought it was better that way: once that type starts to notice you, the next step's trouble.

So we played away on and everything was quite the thing. They didn't bother us and we were quite happy to be ignored even if they had cadged a game off us the night before when they didn't have their own ball with them. Had to let them in of course, or that would have been the last we'd have seen of Tommy's, and it's a stoater. A bladder, know? a real one; think you're really gemm when you play with that, so you do. Yet strangely enough, it wasn't the fact that it was such a good ball that caused it; it could have been any old something that just happened to get in Rab's way when he was on the point of doing a brammer by his way of it.

See, Wullie had lobbed it good and hard and Davey's cousin had missed it. Now, that was what Wullie had meant to do, because you don't kick a ball at the Enemy's goalmouth and expect the keeper to trap it, do you? So of course, Wullie reckoned it was his own fault and we all agreed with him and told him to go and get it.

And that's where the trouble came in.

"Heh, Mikey! Big Mikey MacGloan! That baw, gonnae?" he shouts, and belts off after it across onto the other pitch. As luck would have it, Big Mikey seemed to be in quite a good mood, because he turns round to the bladder, decides it's a nice night or something, and gives it a right good belt. Only trouble was though, he hit it that hard that Wullie had to duck to keep his head in one piece, with the unfortunate result that it bounced off the palings and stoated right back to Rab Forrest's feet. And, as I say, it put him right off his kick.

Now, this Rab Forrest.

Well, he's not like Mikey, not really. I mean, Mikey's a bit of a nutter, and kind of daft, always looking for a bit of fun by his way of it, but he's not bad if you know what I mean. He knows where to stop, know? See this Rab, but? He's mean right through, and pure mental I'd say. It wouldn't surprise me if he ended up inside a loony bin one of these days, murdering his granny for fag money or something.

So anyway, to cut a long story short, he turns round and shouts — well, I'll not tell you exactly, but the gist of it is that Wullie's ma and da aren't married — which is something coming from him, by the way — and that he's going to have to run like a lassie to get his soandso ball back. And as he's saying this he takes a huge swipe at it, and sends it flying right over the palings and into the Circus, where it starts to roll down the hill.

Well, I've never seen anything like it, telling you.

I mean, Wullie can handle himself as I know, because

we've been pals since we were in that wee school, but he's not bothered with that kind of thing usually. Rather than fight, he'll have a laugh about whatever it is that somebody's been saying to him, and generally he's that infectious that whoever it is starts to laugh along with him, and that's the end of the story. Easy-going, you know?

Aye, but not this time.

Maybe it was because it was the end of the holidays as I was saying before and everbody was that wee bit fed up. Or maybe it was because he was browned off with that lot coming in and spoiling a good wee game with the Madrid tactics. Or maybe it was the pair of them put together. I don't know, I wouldn't like to say; but whatever it was, he just lost the head. And I mean completely. Imagine challenging anybody like Rab Forrest? I mean, with Mikey you might get tanked, but it would be sure to be a fair do; but that mental Rab just lays about him with anything that's near to hand, and he gets steamed right in without bothering about the damage he might be doing to somebody. Pure absolute mental, as I was saying.

Well, Wullie did it anyway. We could all see him from where we were, and we heard some sort of shout coming from him — the kind of thing where you can't actually hear what's going on, but you can tell by the sound of it that the bloke's lost the head.

"Heh," goes Tommy, "Ah'm gaun orr therr tae see aboot this. Wullie must be daft ur sumhin, shoutin at that f'lla. E'll get is heid done fur im."

"Aye," I says. "Moan. Mibbe wull kin stoap im daein enihin stupit."

The trouble is in a thing like this, you can't run across to your mates, or the other team thinks you're going to give him handers, so by the time you get there they're all ready, linked up to get pitched into you. And like I say, apart from Big Mikey, it's not just the hands and feet that get used on you. Well, the result of all this was, by the time we'd walked over kind of canny like, the damage had been done. Whatever it was that Wullie had said, Rab was blind angry. His jacket was off, and the pair of them were circling each other with their hands out, ready for the other to make the first move.

Then I thought we were going to get him out of it.

See, we weren't the only ones who'd noticed what was going on. I've told you about the jannie, up and down in his moods and that? Well, Hawkeyes had seen this other crowd

coming in and right enough you can't blame him for
keeping his big nose turned in their direction. I mean, them
and trouble you can smell a mile away.

"Right," he says. "Get; thi loat a yiz. Fyiz want tae
knoack thingmmi oot a each uthur yiz ur welcum. Fact, Ah
hope yiz dae a thingmmi good joab at it so's yizull no be
back tae boathir me fur a foartnight. Cumoan then; get."

"Aw, Mr Preston," goes Wullie," it wiznae me. Wiv been
in here a while an no causin eni trubbil. You know that. It's
this wan, jiss beltin oor baw kiz..."

"Look son, Ah'm no here tae argybargy wi you ur wi
enibdi. Youse boays ur aw thi same iz faur iz Ah'm
cincerned. By Thingmmi, Ah let yiz in here iz a favour,
doan't Ah? Yiz aw know yiz urnae opposed tae get in here
eftir yir twelve? Ih? Yiz kin aw read thi noatice-boards Ah
hope, ih? Eniwey, yiz know noo. So get."

Right enough, he's not bad that way, I'll have to give it
to him for that. As long as you don't make a rammy or a
mess or that, he always does let you play in there in spite of
what the notice says — and to be fair, he still let us all in the
night after. But at the time he was beeling, and you can
understand why, I suppose. Not that it was much comfort for
us then, mind.

But listen, you should have seen Wullie at that. Now, I'd
have thought that this was the kind of time he'd have
calmed down, you know? When somebody who doesn't
really have anything to do with the dispute comes in, it
generally gives you time to get a hold of yourself a bit, and
as I've already said about Wullie, it takes a lot to get him
going. But this must just have been one of those days.

I mean, there's no other word for it. He just hissed.

He went right up to Rab's ugly face, and near enough
spat into his eyes.

"Lissn, yella," he says, "Ah'm jiss aboot uptae here wi
you inaw this thingmmi yiv been gie'n us aw summir. Ah'm
gaun oota this pitch, an Ah'm gaun uptae thi Dump, an if yir
no therr in five minnits Ah'm cumin roon tae yir hoose tae
pull yi oot fae undur yir granny's bed. An see when Ah've
did that? Ah'm gonnae kill yi!"

Well.

There was nothing to say.

We were all that astonished at this, that it should have
come from Wullie and been thrown to Rab and all, one of
the dirtiest fighters any of us would hope never to meet up
with in a lighted street — well, it was just too much. But sure

enough, Wullie turned his back on us and jumped over the palings into the Circus. He took a couple of steps in the direction of the Dump, and then he seemed to remember something he'd forgotten to say.

"An you, Mikey. Ah've nuthin agaynst you, but yid bettir get im tae cum up thi noo ur yill hiv nae pal left tae go roon fur cum thi morra. Aye, an Ah'll say this tae: yid bettir bring they two boays alang wi yi inaw, kiz thirz gonnae be too minny bits fur jiss you tae kerry hame yirsel!"

Mikey turned round to us after that. And what he did was really funny, when you think back on it. What I mean is, he just ignored Rab, and after all it was his fight. But he says to us, and his face was something to see for the admiration that was in it. I've never seen him like that before, not even for himself when he's scored a corker. He just says:

"See that boay, e's goat sum guts, hint e? Ah mean, e must know e's gonnae get thingmmi tankt right intae thi grunn, ih?"

I wasn't so sure about this, but then that just shows you how stupid I can be at times. There was I thinking it would be a reasonable do, Wullie against Rab; and if Wullie could get at Rab before Rab could get at a brick, it would be some contest the way Wullie was looking. But what I'd forgotten was this, what Mikey said next. Quiet like, know? But there was no mistaking what he meant.

"By thi way, boays . Youse urnae thinkin a cumin roon, ur yiz?"

And what he did was this. He came right up to me, and believe me you'd have to be a Dracula or Somebody to stand up to it when Mikey puts that face of his onto yours like that. Then you see, and it's so old a trick you'd think we'd have been prepared for it at our age, he draws back his left hand to punch me bang on the conk if I'm following his eyes right, and just as I'm wondering whether to duck or parry, he lets fly with his right and cops Davey's wee cousin a stoater on the left ear. And by Thingmmi, it must have been sore. The wee cousin apart, we were all that stunned at this and at the realisation of what it meant for Wullie, that we didn't even kid on we were going to try and get him back for it.

The Big F'lla turned round to his mates. Just like a general he is; I'm sure you'd go along with that if you ever saw him in action. It's the way he never looks at them, you know? Just says something in that kind of a way that you couldn't think anybody would even dream of not obeying him. They certainly didn't, anyway.

"Moan, well. Ah'll kerry yir jaickit fur yi Rab — eftir aw,
you're thi wan that's gonnae hiv tae get in therr—furst."

And he gave a laugh that was that creepy, you know. I
mean, even the wee cousin, him that had copped it on the
ear, even he wasn't greeting or that. I mean, he couldn't,
could he? The whole thing was just too big.

I'm not going to make any excuses for myself or the others,
even if they didn't have a wee sister to watch, but what I
can tell you is that all this came from Big Mikey himself
when I met him down at the Co the day after. (Heh, imagine
Big Mikey going the messages for his ma? well, he does.
Must be some woman, that one.) What I mean by that is, if
one of us had been telling it, you might not have believed us
because we'd have been wanting to make out that one of
our boys was as good as he was gemm. But this came
straight from the Big F'lla, the Leader of the Opposition,
you know? So that just makes it all the better.

It seems that Rab and Mikey and the other two — I
never found out their names actually, but I think they were
cousins of one of them, or something — it seems they went
straight round to the Dump as soon as they left us, and sure
enough there was Wullie waiting for them at the top of the
Big Mound where it's nice and flat and hardly anybody can
see what's going on because it's more or less hidden from
the road.

"Yir oan yir ain, wee man," says Mikey to him when
they'd got up beside him. "Yir pals aw hid tae go hame tae
thir beds."

"Well," says Wullie — and by the way, I'm only
reporting this from Big Mikey because Wullie won't even
talk about it. He's like that, sometimes. Funny.

"Well," he goes, "sno therr fight, izit? Ah wiz thi wan
tae dae thi challinge, an it's up tae theym if they want tae
cum ur no......Ur yi right, Rab?"

I suppose, when you think about it, it's not really all that
out of character for Wullie. What I mean is, he might be
easygoing and that. In fact he is as I've said to you I know
well enough; but it's like the way I was telling you about
when he suddenly laughs at something, he's that infectious
that everybody round about starts laughing as well — even
if the joke's against you yourself. I think that must have
been what it must have been with Rab, too. As far as I could
have told you when they left the pitch, Rab wasn't
particularly interested. I'm not saying he was yellow the
way Wullie had called him that, because I'm sure he

thought at the time that Wullie was easy meat for mincing; it's just that I think he'd have been just as pleased if Tommy had gone for the ball and that would have made an end to the story. But when Wullie started in at him that way, that's what I mean about the infection. Works the other way as well.

"Right," shouts Rab, "moan well. Ah hivnae goat aw night."

He tore off his jacket and threw it in the direction of the Big F'lla.

"You inaw, son. It's jiss yir face Ah'm gonnae rip, no yir claes. Eftir aw, a paupir like your maw cannae go aboot buyin yi a new jaickit ivri five year."

If that didn't goad him, the next must just have been the end. Though mind you, if I'd been on the receiving end of something like that, I reckon I'd have seen so red that that would have been an end of my science before it had even begun. Know what I mean? Somebody asks you to take your jacket off, you don't expect him to land you one in the mouth when your hands are in a fankle with your sleeves: and that's just what the thingmmi did, though I suppose Wullie should have known him well enough to have expected it.

Anyway, did he lose the head? Not Wullie, thank you. He just stepped back a bit, shook himself free of the jacket and stood ready to see what the score was going to be. I can see him actually, the careful wee thingmmi, and he'd be quite unaware of the blood that was oozing out of his lower lip where the teeth had gone through; just be standing back, eying him up, knowing from then on that no trick was going to be too dirty for the other team to use. It probably came as a bit of a relief to him if I know Wullie, because he always likes to give the other man the benefit of the doubt till he knows different. You know, the kind of referee your da talks about in the old days when the game was fair and unbiasedly, judged by their way of it? But the trick with the jacket would have done for that, all right. Now, you see, he could stop up the wee bit of his mind that was telling him he was up against a bloke, and so he could put his whole attention to watching the unpredictabilities of this thing that was facing him, this pure animal.

That's what he is that Rab, you know.

Well, that was it. There was the pair of them, the one circling the other again like they were a couple of Cassius Clays or whatever his name is now, and I can just imagine it

from watching their footwork on the field. One thing about
Wullie though, when you field a big team, they always put
him at the back because he's a rare defender. You know,
just that right mixture of wait-and-see, but only wait-and-
see till the first mistake is made by the forwards on the other
side — and see then? No stopping him.

And that's just what he did, according to the Big F'lla.

"Aye," he says to me the next day in the Co, "byootifull
tae watch, know whit Ah mean? That's how e's alive thi noo,
an Ah'm no jokin. See, Rab cum intae im wi thi left haun
drew back iz if e wiz gonnae pit wan oan Wullie right aboot
thi middil a is phizog, an yi know how Rab kin be that
frightnin, yon mentil wey that yi hiv tae be a hero ur a
needgit tae staun up tae that look oan im? Aye, well Wullie
did that. Jiss ignore tit iz if e knew ixackly whit wiz cumin;
and lookin back oan it noo, Ah reckin e must iv.

"See, Ah've saw Rab at this afore, an whit e diz is e gets
thi uthur f'lla that feart a that haun a his, and when thi eyes
an thi parry goes up, oot cums thi right fit — straight intae
thi thingmmi. Bang. Well Ah mean, it's a pure mentil kick
an usyalli that's thi fight iz good iz ower right away. E jiss
gies thum a couplaboot thi face wi is boot, an kinna walks
away hame tae is granny's.

"But iz Ah say, Wullie seen it cumin. An whit e done
wiz, e waitit fur that fit, seen it a mile away, an jiss iz cool iz
ye like goat a haud ae it in Rab's mid-swing. An see, Rab
wiz gaun that hard eniwey that aw Wullie hid tae dae wiz
gie it a wee twist — an by Thingmmi, Ah thoat e wiz
straight hame tae is granny's right inuff — doon the close
chimney an through thi bedroom ceilin!"

Well as you might imagine, I wasn't exactly unhappy to
hear this, especially seeing as I hadn't had the heart to go
and see Wullie at home in the morning, because to tell you
the right truth about it, I was frightened to see what I
thought I would have to. And I might as well be honest
about this and all — I was scared he wouldn't be speaking
to me ever again.

"An wiz that thi end ae it , Mikey?" says I, all breathless
and that, you know, waiting to hear the juicy bits if there
were any more to come onto the end of this. And by here,
there weren't half all right.

"Well," he goes, "that wiz thi beginnin a thi end if yi
like, kiz...... Here, wait a minnit! Is that thi right time? Ah'll
hiv tae get roon hame wi thi auld wummin's fags rAh'll get
killt!"

"Naw!" I goes, near screaming, you know? "That cloack's olwiz at least five minnits fast, Mikey. At least five!"

He kind of looked at me and of course he must have known I'd just made that up on the spur of the moment so's he'd wait till the story was at an end. Still, I think I was the first person he'd had a chance to tell it to, and right enough it's not surprising that he wanted to make sure he had a really appreciative audience for the first go. It was some tale.

"Wiz that thi end ae it, yi wir askin? Well, it wiz an it wiznae, fyi know whit Ah mean. Lookin back oan it noo an seein whit happind eftir, it wiz thi end right inuff, an Ah think Wullie knew it tae. See, whit happind wi Rab wiz, e jiss loast thi heid.

"Noo you know iz well iz Ah dae," he goes, and this is another one of those strange comments of his — strange coming from him, I mean, and about one of his own boys, you know?

'You know iz well iz Ah dae that Rab's mentil at thi best a times — Ah mean, yiv seen me hivin tae take im in haun in case e murdurs sumbdi, hivint yi?"

"Aye, Mikey," I goes, and it's true enough...... but that's another story, maybe. Anway, "Aye," I says, just hardly able to contain myself for the excitement, if you follow me.

"Well, Ah thoat Ah wiz gonnae hiv tae get in therr lass night tae stoap im fae pullin Wullie's heid aff kiz, yi see, e wiz really hurtit, so e wiz. Noo, Ah doan't right know whithir it wiz thi wey e'd fell oan thi grunn ur whithir it wiz thi wey Wullie hid goat a haud a is leg an gied it that coup that pit im oan is back, but by Thingmmi Rab couldnae staun oan that fit when e goat izsel up.

"Dae yi want tae caw it a day well, ya mentil crippell?" says Wullie tae im when e sees im strugglin tae is feet like that, an e says it aw kinna cruel like, know? rubbin it in an that? Ah've nivir saw im like that afore, neethir Ah hiv. Eniwey, yi kin imagine whit that done tae Rab. E lets oot this great thingmmi shout, Ah mean it wiznae wurds ur enihin like that; merr like a grilla's warcry, ur yir da wi thi indigestiun, know? But nae wurds. Nuthin. Jiss this scream an e starts lookin aboot izsel, an Ah knew whit that wiz fur.

"Ih ?

"Aye, too right it wiz. Thi biggist thingmmi chib e could lay is hauns oan. But by here, it wiz iz if Wullie wantit tae make im really loass thi heid tull therr wiz nuthin left a is wee bit sanity ataw. E sees im hobblin ower tae this bit hauf brick that's caught is eye, an insteid a pickin wan up izsel relse gaun fur a stick ur that, e jiss lets Rab get tae aboot a ninch ae it, then e jumps ower aside im an, dainty iz yi like, pits is fit undur it an knoacks it ower thi side a thi mound.

'Ah'm gonnae kill you, ya wee thingmmi!' shouts Rab, an A thoat e wiz inaw, so Ah did. E jiss flung izsel at Wullie an goat a haud ae im roon aboot thi neck, an that wiz thi perr a thum doon oan thi grunn.

"But therr wiz nae hope.

"See, Wullie wiz calm, know whit Ah mean? E wiz aw therr. But see Rab? Mentil. Pure nuthin left in is concentratiun. Whit Ah mean is, it wiz a foregone conclusiun. Thir rollin aboot oan thi grunn therr, right? Naebdi's oan thi tap — then wan minnit wan a thum's up, next minnit thi uthur, an so it's gaun oan; nif yi hidnae saw whit hid went oan afore yi might uv thoat it wiz enibdi's gemm. But this wiz thi whole point.

"Wullie seems tae let Rab get oan thi tap fur good. E's haudin oantae Rab's hauns so's e canne dae eni damidge wi thum, an while Rab's concentratin oan tryin tae get thum away, Wullie looks fur Rab's twistit fit, gets a haud ae it, an jiss gies it thi most biggist thingmmi kick yiv ivir saw in yir hale thingmmi life!"

He stopped and looked at me, and his face seemed to have transformed in the telling so's he was right back there the night before, reliving it all again.

"Aw, it wiz gallus, man. Pure gallus. Rab starts rollin aboot thi grunn in pure absaloot agony. 'Awmammydaddy, mammydaddy!' e's gaun. An Wullie jiss jumps oan thi tap ae im, pits is knees oan is shoodirs so's e cannae move, an gets stuck right intae im wi thi baith a is hauns. Wan two, wan two, wan eftir thi uthur till therr wiz praktiklli nuthin left a thi bampot...... Well, that's a nexaggeratiun, but e did loass two teeth an is nose is aw squinti this moarnin.

"Heh, Ah'm gonnae get killt fae ma ma! Lookit thi time!"

Oh, I tell you, I was that proud of Wullie that I near let Mikey go without asking him why. Actually, he was halfway round the corner and I had to run to catch up with him.

"Heh Mikey" I shouts. "Wait a minnit, gonnae? Lissn, Ah mean, e's wan a your boays, int e, thi wan yi go roon fur?"

"Aye," goes Mikey, "asright...... how?"

"Well, Ah jiss thoat that eftir yiz left thi pitch lass night, rimembir? Ah thoat...... Aw cumoan, yi know whit Ah mean, Mikey......

"Did Rab no shout fur handirs?"

Well, he just looked at us that way I was telling you about, admiration and that all over his face. At the memory of it, I suppose.

"Aw sure, e shoutit, yi know whit he's like. But Ah says tae thi uthur two wi wirnae gaun in. An neethir we did."

He glanced over at me, and he must have seen the way I was looking that bit puzzled or something, because he says:

"But lissn, dae yi no undurstonn whit Ah've been oan aboot? Eh? Ah mean, it wiz pure thingmmi gallus, so it wiz.

"A boay like that, man?

"Pure gallus!"

Our Merry

What I mean is, I know Andy's my mate and maybe you shouldn't criticise your pals too much, because then the folk that aren't his mates can sometimes take advantage of what you say and so it gets back to him — and then where are you? Sometimes he goes too far though: I'll just put it that way.

I've got a wee sister called Merry and that's really what the trouble's about. I've seen an awful lot of sisters worse than she is, but that's not saying much for a girl is it? Always hanging about and wanting to be let in. Still, her excuse is this, and I suppose it's quite a reasonable one if you can be reasonable about things like that.

You see, we live in a wee bit that's off the road from everbody else in the scheme. A cul de sac ma da calls it— you know what that is? one of they roads that have an opening at one end for you to get in by but, once you get to the other end, there's nothing there, you know? a dead end? So if you don't want to spent the rest of your life wandering about like an idiot, you have to go back where you came from, cross the road and find another way out. But that's where the trouble comes, the trouble about Merry — because that's the main road, and a dual carriageway at that.

Now I can perfectly understand why ma's like that, that worried way, because it is an awful busy road, there's no getting away from it. In fact, I can speak on that probably better than most folk because it was really me that caused the bother I'll be telling you about in a minute, although it wasn't my fault if you see what I mean. No, that's not very clear. What happened was that when I was just started school in the babies' class, ma always used to take me in, and I suppose that's fair enough when you're only a wee bloke of five or that. Anyway, Merry wasn't born then and ma had nothing else to do all day , so it was up to her. After I'd been there about six months though, she started not feeling very well in the mornings, so I remember her taking me out one day up to the corner and going through the drill — mind all that stuff you used to get about not forgetting to look left and right and that? Well.

I thought this was great, of course. A wee guy like me being allowed to cross the road on his own, and that one of

the busiest roads in the town! And I was good at it too, even
if I say it myself, because when the time came that I nearly
got hit it wasn't my fault at all. It was this f'lla on a
motorbike, and the reason I never saw him was he was
going too fast. Not that I remember, of course, but that
apparently is what the judge said to him when he took his
licence away for two years. However, I was lucky, and I
don't deny it, and whatever I said to her at the time, I was
really glad that ma started taking me back to school again
till she went into hospital, and then arranged for Andy's
mother to take me in along with him in the mornings.

"Aw, nivir agayn, Mrs Montrose," I remember her
saying to her that first morning. "Thi doactur says Ah'm
lucki Ah didnae hiv a miskerridge."

"Aye, Ah know. That road's a cryin disgrace, so it is,"
says Andy's ma. "But doan't you worry yir heid aboot
enihin, hen. Ah'll see thi wee f'lla awright tull yi get oot —
then by thi time thi additiun's big inuff tae be gaun tae
school itsel, Andy and him'll be that bit biggir inuff tae take
it in in thi moarnins. An that'll save a loat a trubbil, wintit?"

Well, it turned out to be Merry, and it had to be taken to
school right enough.

So, here's where this trouble is, then. Now, I was all
right. I mean, here are we living in this 'cul de sac' as I was
saying; precious few houses so precious few folk, and of
course that means precious few folk to play with. It was just
pure coincidence that Andy and I were the same age, and I
suppose when you come to think of it it's a purer fluke that
we get on together most of the time. I mean, when you look
around at the folk in your class, well that's about forty
usually and roughly half of them is boys (though it normally
seems there's twice as many lassies the noise they make), so
that gives you twenty mates. But how many of them do you
get on with? really get on with? Maybe I'm nasty or
something, though I don't think so because the others are
just about the same this way, but you can count on me
having a fight or an argument with at least one of them in a
week. And that's not counting them you wouldn't look at
twice, not even if you were short of a man.

Anyway, what I mean by all that is, Andy and I have
always got on together apart from the odd time when you
get fed up and kind of funny, so that's all right. So when we
were wee we didn't have to girn about our mas to get taken
into the park or across the road to meet somebody on the

other side of the carriageway because that was where all
the boys and the games and that were.

But Merry's different. I mean, there are only the three of
us kids in our bit, right? And for a start, Merry's only five
and we're grown up compared with her; then second, she's
a lassie, isn't she? What more can you say?

Well, here's a bit of it.

Merry's not allowed to cross the road on her own, and
that's fair enough because she'd probably get knocked over
if not killed the same way that I nearly was, and she doesn't
deserve that. No, really; she's quite nice even though she
has her limitations what with being a girl and wee as well
and all. I'm quite tolerant that way. But the thing is, if she
can't get away to see her pals, what does she do? She can't
swop scraps with herself or any of the daft things you see
them doing in the playground, can she? And maybe you
can tie one end of your rope to a lamp post and rocky it, but
you've had it if you want to caw and skip at the same time.
No, I feel quite sorry for her, and I can really sympathise at
times. That was probably why we let her into the game that
was the start and finish of it that afternoon.

See, Andy's garden's just about the same size as ours,
fact they're all the same round our way, but his has got a
wee slope for some reason. His father hates it, I can tell you,
and sometimes on a Sunday afternoon or that you'll hear
Andy's ma shouting out to him to mind his language, and
she doesn't care whether that soandso slope is the only
soandso slope in the whole soandso street, but just
remember there are weans about and set them a good
example. Anyway, the thing is about that slope, it's great
for Best Falls. No, really. Whoever's the sniper can get in all
snug and that behind the garden hut, and then whoever's
not hit can come running up over the top of that wee bit
mound, and you get some great tumbles that way.
Handstands and wulkies and everything. And that's what
we're doing that day when Merry comes wandering round
the path and looks at us. Just looks, you know how they
sometimes do when they're wee? As if the whole world's
against them, the way they stand with their thumbs in their
mouths, the doll cooried into one arm and its blanket
trailing on the ground? All pathetic like.

Actually, it was Andy that asked her, not me, and that's
what I mean about him not being bad and that. He's really
quite kind to her, considering she's not even his sister and
just another lassie, you know?

"Heh, Merry," he goes. "Want a gemm a best faws?"

Well, did she want a game of best falls? I wish you could have seen the look on her face when he said that. Like as if God had been speaking to that Virgin Mary all over again, she was that delighted.

"Aw aye!" she says. "That'd be great!"

"Right then, " goes Andy. "you kin go het furst, well. Jiss tae get yi use tae thi kinna faws yi kin dae. Hiv yi ivir saw thi gemm afore?"

"Aw aye," she goes, throwing away her doll and blanket and charging up to the hut like King Billy as if he's just seen the Pope — and him with his back turned at that.

"Aye, Ah've saw thi boays in ma class playin roon thi back a thi dinnir school. Youse hiv tae faw aboot an Ah've goat tae decide whit wan a yiz goes doon the best, hint Ah?"

"Asright, Merry," says I, chuffed that she knows enough about the thing not to disgrace me in front of my pal. "Moan well, an get intae yir hideoot.".

So in she goes and we get started. She must have been watching the boys right enough, because she really could make the noise, you know? She decides she's a machine-gun nest, just so's we've no chance of escape, I suppose — though come to think about it, this is about the only game I know where you go out your way to get shot, instead of trying to avoid it.

"Hi-hi-hi-hi-hiiiiiiiiiiii! Pchchchcheeeeow ! Pchchch-cheeeeow! Hi-hi-hi-hi-hiiiiiiiiiiiiii!!!"

Well, you come up against something as lethal as that and you'd be dead pretty soon and all, I'd say. So we come tearing up, Andy and I, and we each do what we hope's the best one, because even if Merry is only a lassie and wee and that, this is the first time we've ever competed one against the other, if you know what I mean. Before that it had only been me shooting him and then him shooting me and then me taking over again — and on it would go. But there'd never been this idea that you had to go up and exert yourself, and really try to make whoever it was realise that your fall was far and away the better of the two.

Know what I mean?

Anyway, I don't know whether it was because he did a bellyflapper which I wouldn't have done to win any old competition, not even in the baths, or whether it was because she had to pick him, but Andy won that round. When I say she had to pick him, what I mean is that I was only her brother and so she sort of knew me anyway; but Andy was nothing to her, not a relation or that, and apart from being polite, she was grateful to him for asking her if she wanted to join in when she was all fed up, and he didn't need to because it was his garden anyway.

That was fine then, and Andy goes behind the shed again and takes up his position as sniper.

Now, to give her her due, she tried. Really tried. I suppose she was that glad at being granted the honour of joining in that she thought she'd better try and make as good a show as possible so's we'd give her another game some time, and not just think she was that daft that we had to humour her now and again. But that was the trouble, I suppose; she just tried too hard.

What I thought I'd do was I'd let her go on first so's she could have as much space as possible to try out the fall, because as far as I knew she'd never done it before even though she might have watched how the game was meant to be played; and also, I was hoping that if she didn't make an absolute real fool of herself, then Andy would pick her that time even if what she did wasn't a patch on mine who's been playing the game for years. As I say though, she must just have tried too hard.

See, she ran up to Andy and of course we're both crackshots anyway, so he reckoned it to be a point of honour only to take one aim, one deadeye shot with a .303, and always get his man with that single go.

"Yiv goat tae save yir ammo, hint yi?" he says. "Ah mean, yi nivir know when yi might hiv tae staun up tae a great big attack wi aw thi enimy platoon agaynst yi at wance?"

So Merry goes tearing up to him like he was the ice cream man just about to move away and Andy, all casual like, leans back on his right elbow, steadies his gun, and takes one shot.

"Pchch!" he goes.

And Merry falls, screaming.

Actually, I was surprised how good it was. You know how important it is not just to fall, but to make the right noises as you're going down? At least, I always give points to them when I'm hit and there's mabe three or four folk playing instead of just a courtesy game between the two of you—like you sometimes get at school, instead of just in the mate's garden and that. And anyway, apart from that, there are some folk who don't mabe fall all that well, but the

contortions and antics they get up to when they're on the
ground are sometimes that good, like John Wayne when you
think he's going to go on dying for ever and ever, that you
have to take that into account for your final assessment of
the game.

And here, Merry was good at the both of them, the
noises and the rolling about and that, even though her fall
was maybe a bit amateur.

That of course was where the trouble came in. You see,
what we didn't realise Andy and I, was that she wasn't
kidding. I mean, this screaming and yelling goes on and on
for what seems like hours, and eventually Andy has to say to
her:

"Awright Merry, that wiz quite good. But gonnae get yir
carciss oot thi wey tull Danny gets his go?"

But no. She doesn't move.

"Heh Merry," I goes, "gonnae move, ih? Did yi no hear
Andy? Ah've goat nae room fur ma faw."

Still nothing, and still this shouting and bawling and
screaming till it gets so loud and it's going on so long, that
Andy's ma appears at the kitchen window.

"Heh, whits thi maittir oot therr? Sumbdi hurtit?"

Well actually, that was the first time that Andy or I had
thought, I think, that maybe there was, if you'll credit that;
so we kind of look at each other and then start moving over
across from where we are. Right enough at that too, it
wasn't just yelling she's doing when you get close enough to
see. Her face is all wet with tears and there's no doubt about
it that she's crying. And not just a girn, either.

"Whit's thi maittir, Merry," I says, "hiv yi hurtit yirsel,
hen?"

She didn't even stop then, and when I bent down to see
what it was, see if she'd fallen over something or something,
I noticed she was lying on her arm.

"Izit yir errum, Merry?" I goes, and tries to get hold of
her to lift her up a wee bit till she's sitting, and we can get a
proper good look at her. And the noise she lets out at that!
You'd have thought the end of the world was coming in a
minute, the way she belted out that yell!

"Aw naw, doan't touch it! Doan't touch ma errum!
Awww nawww! Nawww! Take me hame tae ma mammy!"

By this time of course, Mrs Montrose has come into the
garden and up to us to see what all the noise and carry on's
about, because you can imagine it's got an awful lot worse
since she poked her head out of the window.

"Moan, oot thi way youse boays tull Ah hiv a look. Whit izit hen, ma wee sowel? Let's hiv a wee look at yi.

"Aw, fur God's sake! wid yi look at that! Thi bone's came right through thi flesh at ur elba!

"Here you, Danny. Away an get yir mammy tae stey wi thi wee thing so's Ah kin get up tae thi phone boax fur a nambulince."

"By thingmmi, that's thi lass time A ivir play wi a lassie in ma life," says Andy. And I thought the way he was kicking away at half bricks as if they were wee chuckies, that that was maybe the last pair of boots he might ever get bought in his life and all. Nearly nothing left of them about the toes.

"Aye," I goes, kind of drawing it out like a great big sigh. I didn't want to say much more about it, because after all it was my sister that had caused us all the trouble, so I felt twice as guilty twice over — if you know what I mean.

See, to put you in the picture, what had happened was this .The ambulance had come right away, about twenty minutes or that after Andy's mother had called it — the phone box being working for once — and so ma and Merry went off to the hospital leaving me to get my dinner at Mrs Montrose's seeing as they didn't know when they'd be getting back. And at that time, the time I'm telling you about the next day, Andy and I were wishing they'd never got back at all.

This was on our way home from school, dragging it out as long as possible because our punishment—punishment mark you, as if it was our fault that a lassie was gawky enough to break her arm and us being good enough to give her a game — our punishment was that we weren't to get out after school for a whole week. Aye, and not even be allowed to watch the telly, either.

"Confinet tae barricks," ma da says, as he put me up to my room after tea. "Solitri confinement, son."

Actually, I think he was on our side to tell you the truth, realising it was an accident and that, but what could he do? Or Andy's father either, come to that? I mean, they were just as bad as us, up against a conspiracy of lassies and women.

"Aye, an yi know whit else?" Andy goes.

"Aw naw, doan't tell us thirz merr!"

"Aw aye," he says. "An wait tull yi hear it. 'An whit's

merr, ' ma ma says lass night, 'if a cerrfull wee lassie like
Merry kin go aboot brekkin ur errum, youse two daft boays
ull probbli en dup brekkin yir necks. So fae noo oan, when
yiz ur playin, yizull play in Danny's gerdin'."

"Aw, yir jokin," I goes.

"Aw naw Ah'm urnae," he says. "Jiss you wait tull yi get
hame an yill get tellt awright."

"Aw thingmmi. That's no ferr. Ah mean, it's no jiss that
wi hivnae goat a hut in oor gerdin — wi hivnae evin goat a
slope!"

"Aye, you're telln me," says Andy.

"Ach, Ah'm no playin!"

And that was how it turned out and all, right enough. When
the week was by and we were allowed out after school
again, it had to be either the street or our garden, and
believe me, if you'd seen our garden you'd realise why it
wasn't fair. It's a reasonable size, I suppose, but my da's got
this thing about the rise in the cost of living or something,
and practically everywhere you look there's something
growing. And where there's something growing, you can't
go — potatoes here, a patch of rhubarb over there, and
things like peas and strawberries and thingmmi knows all
what coming up all over the place. In other words, all we're
allowed to use is that wee bit my ma for her drying
green, and I don't need to tell you that she's got something
hanging out just about every day there's any wee bit sun at
all — just the times you're wanting a game at heidies or
three-and-in or something.

So of course, we just had to give it up as a bad job and
play in the street, and you know how that cramps your style
if you fancy doing a nifty save; either you risk skinning your
arm or breaking your neck on the pavement — or you let the
thing go right past you.

Terrible, so it was.

And then of course there was Merry.

Well, I don't suppose it was her fault that she'd broken
her arm. Not really. I don't even think that Andy was daft
enough to think she'd done it on purpose so's we wouldn't be
let enjoy ourselves; but what could we do? I mean, whether
she'd wanted it or not, she'd ruined our games in the
garden, so that was it.

After a couple of days ma let her go back to school
because the stookie on her arm was set strong enough to

stop her doing it any more harm, and anyway she said it wasn't sore any more, just itchy; so I suppose she must have been telling the truth. You know how soft the lassies are when they get a wee knock — think it's the end of the world so they do, just because they've got a skinned pinky or something. Just looking for sympathy, I think.

But apart from that, Merry was having this great time at school during the day. Well, it's only the babies' class she's in, so none of them's had the time to get old enough to break themselves in the way we are; I mean, hardly a month going by without scmebody snapping something, whether it's an arm or a leg or whatever it is. So, she was the first, and she was having this marvellous time because Miss Simpson — that's the Infants' Mistress we all get when we start the school in the first year—was all for making a great fuss of her because she was so wee; and all her mates, of course, writing their names on the stookie for a souvenir the way you do. Well actually, it's just drawings if you can even call them that the way they scribble at that age, because of course you don't learn to print, never mind real writing, till you're into Primary 2. At least, that's the way it works in our place.

So. That's just to let you know that although we couldn't talk to her at nights because she was the cause of all our trouble, I didn't feel quite so bad about being her big brother and all, and you know what they say about blood being thicker than water. I wasn't feeling guilty because she was having this great time during the day seeing she was that wee bit different, and the centre of attention with her mates.

And that was how it started that night with the kitten. What I mean is, she was sitting on the pavement with her feet in the siver, because you can do that in our bit seeing as how just about the only motor that comes up is Victor's the icey's. We were playing keepie-up I think it was, trying to let on that she wasn't there and pretending we were having such a great time that we didn't even notice her being all lonely and that again, because this time we had decided we wouldn't even talk to her, never mind ask her if she wanted a game.

But suddenly there was this yell. I mean, it wasn't the kind of yell she'd let out that time she fell or that, it was more like as if you'd gone to bed on Christmas Eve and forgotten what night it was. You follow me? so that when you woke up the next morning you got a hundred times better a surprise than usual?

Of course, we turned round to see what it was.

"Aw, lookit yi," she was saying, "urint yi luvvli? Aw so yi ur, so yi ur — byootifull. Jiss pure byoo — ti— full!"

And so it was and all.

See, she had this wee kitten in her hands, and it was that toty you'd have thought it shouldn't have been away from its mother. I mean, I don't know anything about cats mind you, but this couldn't have been any more than maybe about six inches long, and it certainly was the nicest wee cat I've ever seen. It was pure glossy black, all over, just black: except for this one single wee bit that was dead white on its right hand or I suppose you should say right forepaw, and that was that white that it made the rest of the black seem as if it was even blacker because of the contrast. You should have seen it, but. A wee beaut.

We went over, of course.

"Heh, that's a wee stoatir," says Andy, and bends down to get a stroke at it.

"Lee it alane, you!" goes Merry, just as sudden as that; screaming and cuddling it real tight the way she does with her dolls. "Yir no tae touch it, awright? Awright? Ur you neethir! Kiz it's mines!"

"Heh, wait a minnit, Merry," I goes. "Whit dyi mean, it's yours? It's probbli jiss a stray or that and that means it's naebdi's...... relse if it's no a stray, it's sumbdi else's."

Well, you should have seen her when I said that! Looking more like a tiger that the wee cat did itself, and we've just done nature in school and they're all the same family —you can see the resemblance, right enough.

"It's no . Smines an it's naebdi else's! Naebdi else's! An naebdi else's gonnae get touchin it sept ma mammy eethir!"

And up she gets, pushing this wee thing that hard into her chest that I thought she was going to crush it on her plaster, and she runs into the house with it leaving me and Andy just standing there, too frightened with her screaming and that to do very much about anything.

Eventually Andy turns round to me though, and he says:

"See your wee sistir? Ah thoat Ah'd went aff ur afore, so Ah did. But see noo? Ah've went right aff ur. Right thingmmi aff ur!"

I could see what he meant, I suppose, specially in the light of what went on over the next two or three days.

You see, I suppose you're a bit like me, always wanted

a puppy or a kitten or something? Mice and hamsters and that? And of course everytime you bring it up, it's always:

"Too messy!"

Or:

"Yid get fed up wi it eftir a week an then muggins here wid hiv tae look eftir it, an take it fur its walks and that."

And when you say that you wouldn't, honest you wouldn't, and look at soandso because he loves his and never gets tired of it:

"Ach, it's agaynst thi lease a thi hoose eniwey. If thi Corpiratiun fun oot wi hid a nanimal, wid get put oot."

And then you say it's not fair because everbody else has got one — and so they have when you think about it — then's when you get the real truth of the matter:

"Look, yir no gettin wan, right? an that's aw therr is aboot it. Noo, gie's peace, gonnae?"

Pure badness so it is. Just because they can't be bothered.

But Merry got that kitten anyway, after me campaigning for years!

Rich, ih?

"Mibbe yill no kin keep it, hen," ma says to her. "Ah mean, it might be sumbdi's that's jiss goat away fae its hoose. But wull hing oantae it tull Ah ask aboot, then if it isnae enibdi's yi kin hiv it fur yir ain."

Ach, maybe it was because she'd broken her arm and her being wee and that that did it, to make up for not having any pals about to cheer her up; and I can understand that maybe they gave her it for the company. But still, it wasn't fair. Lassies always get everything. Spoiled, they are. That's what I'd say.

She loved that cat mind you, for all the time she had it, and I think that's maybe what made it worse about Andy at the end of it, maybe why I got so annoyed at him.

And strange to say, I mean you know what cats are like? Independent and that, never come up and give you a paw, or you can't train them to do gemm things like fetch a ball or carry the messages or that, know? Like a dog? And this thing was no exception as far as that was concerned. But the thing was, it was affectionate to Merry. It knew, I mean it really knew, who she was, and it seemed to tolerate her in a way I've never known a cat to make the difference between human beans before.

Of course, she never let it out of her sight. Never even played with her dolls when she had it. In fact if you'd

believe it, she even took it into school one day because Miss
Simpson asked her to let them all see it.

See the things you get away with in Primary 1!

Mind you, it was a holy terror, a Street Arab my da
called it, and I think it must have been a stray right enough.
For all its size, it knew how to use itself. Claws out, teeth in,
scratch and tear and rip and bite — any time you could get
Merry to let you get a clap at it. And even with her, though
it never actually drew blood the way it did from the rest of
us, it still played gey rough. She encouraged it of course,
there's no denying that, and the way she used to torment it
was something awful — so that it would box her as she
called it, and that's just what it looked like, actually. Angry
and annoyed, or maybe it was just kidding, I don't know, it
would get up on its wee back legs and she would get down
in the front of it, and then she'd use the hand that wasn't
gammy to get belted in at it so's it would fight back: one,
two; left paw, right paw; left paw, right paw, for all the
world as if it was defending the flyweight Lonsdale.

But that wasn't its best one.

"Heh!" she shouts one day, just as Andy and I were
leaving for the baths. "Heh, cumere tae yiz see this! It's is
new trick!"

Well, seeing as this was one of the few times she
actually asked us to come and have a look at her precious
beast, and seeing as we were more curious than proud the
way we should have been, we went over for a wee quick
gander.

"Whit's it daein noo well, Merry?"

"Well, jiss lookit this. Right Blackie, cumoan; gie's a
fight."

And she starts in to boxing at it again.

"Ach Merry," I says, "wiv saw it daein that afore. Wi
know it kin boax awright."

"Ah, but wait tae yiz see this."

And it really was funny, right enough. What she did
was to inveigle it into its boxing match as usual, and there
was nothing out the way in that; but that was only the
beginning because this time, when she's got it carried away
and running around like a mad thing and that, she puts her
hand up underneath its back legs and shouts:

"Wulkies! Tummul yir wulkies, Blackie, gawn! Up
'nower!"

And by Thingmmi, so it did and all, the funniest thing
you've ever seen in your natch. Aw, we were in kinks, I'm

telling you. Up in the air it went, spinning backwards, and she gives it just a wee flick of the wrist so's it does a double somersault and lands on it's feet. Talk about funny!

"Aw here, that's gemm, Merry," says Andy. "Gonnae gie's a shot?"

"Naw!" she shouts. And I mean, he should have known by this time. "Nae shots, so you jiss lee im alane. Ah'll dae it agayn fyiz ur wantin tae see it."

And of course the cat was that daft it just came back for more every time. We were both itching to get our hands on it, it was that gallus watching it, but of course that was impossible as far as Merry was concerned.

I'm glad now, and I'll tell you that all right.

"See how clevir e is? Olwiz lands oan is feet — doan't yi, son?"

So she gives it another wee skelp and up he goes, twirls round twice, lands dead on his four paws right enough; then he looks kind of dazed for a wee minute, but tops it all charging in at the attack again.

And so she obliged.

Up and over, attack; up and over, attack; up and over, attack.

Then he began to seem to be getting a wee bit fly for it. Not that he stopped mind you, because he was having just as much fun as the rest of us and maybe even more for all I know; but he seemed to be learning something — what I mean is that instead of lying down on his belly and wriggling his back legs to let you know he was just about ready to spring, he started stalking off with his back to her and watching out the corner of his eye. And then, when he thought she was least expecting it, he'd make this great sudden big dash and try and grab a hold of her hand with his teeth. Aye, and talk about wild? he did it once or twice and all.

I think that's what it was, actually. I mean, she got just about as excited as him not knowing what was coming next or whether she was going to get nipped or that, so her reactions weren't maybe just as calculated as they'd been before he started this wee bit tactic of his. Anyway, whether it was that or not, it was a terrible shock when it came.

See, he comes charging in as usual, and of course over he goes; but that last time, you need to understand, he lands facing her dead, so he doesn't have to go through any palaver at all about facing up or pretending he's going away and not playing any more. He's just there. Dead on

perfectly positioned for attack. And so he jumps — right
away, not giving her any chance for thought.

Crack!

And that was just what it sounded like, too. Up he goes
again, flying almost this time, and lands on his back —
which was warning enough even if we hadn't noticed the
noise before he started sailing.

"Aw naw, Ah didnae mean it," she starts, sobbing and
screaming and that, "Ah didnae: It wiz jiss that he come in
that quick, Ah hit im wi thi wrang haun!"

I mean, he's just lying there, of course, and so Andy
goes over and gives him a prod with his sanny. Rigid, he
seemed to me.

Andy turns round to her, and her with her eyes wide
opened, sobbing away to herself quiet like and looking at
him just to hear said out what she knows fine already.

He looks over from where he is. And then, dead, dead
quiet, he just says:

"See you, Merry? Ah nivir thoat a lassie wid a hid thi
guts."

Birthday

I wonder if it is the crutch and the peg alone. Or the cat companion, perched familiarly upon the right and traditionally parrot shoulder. Or the combination of the pair. Similar to the fearful attraction of the adult deathmask when first seen by a young chimpanzee of the same species. (I speak of the innocents, for the moment.) The magnetism of the familiar and the horrific pull of thanatos, combining to destroy the death of fear in a receiving consciousness.

Or perhaps they imagine that refusal to converse would unleash the fury of deformity and, since my hands are palpably strong and my equilibrium evidently sure-footed, that life would be not so much squeezed from them finally as that a continuing reminder to their heartlessness would be inflicted in the form of a visible and permanent scar. They would become the refusal; the future, refusal for them.

Again, the cat might be trained to sling itself malevolently in the direction of any possible slighting on its mate. Not its protector obviously, since that in itself implies a submissiveness in him which is not there and which lack, therefore, renders his present docility on my shoulder all the more bizarrely disquieting.

Or perhaps they like me simply, and these erratta merely spice the meat, add aroma to the foretaste.

The histories of peg and cat are interesting. Or at least I find them so, in as much as they seem now to be permanant contingencies of my existence, if not essentially of me. Possibly they are complementary, too.

The peg is the result of an accident for which gender typing as much as childish curiosity must take the conscience. My sister was not permitted to translate anal complexities into the unladylike collection and orderly compilation of steam engine numbers, whereas I was encouraged with the cursory injunction of care, and use of native intelligence. The ethic of competition was strong in our neighbourhood however, and did not allow of the glimpse of an engine and the checking of its serial number in the official dictionary of trains.The numerals themselves had to be seen. Bref, I was at once honest and slow, for which virtue and birthright severally, I exchanged a left foot and its subsequently gangrenous shin. Whether the precocity of my adolescence sprang from a compensatory drive on my part as well as from the feminine gaming alluded to above, is impossible to tell now; greater or lesser attractiveness can be a retrospectively moot point only. Suffice to say that never at any time did I masturbate. Myself, that is.

The cat is curious.

He sprang from a doorway one day as I hobbled past it to a relevant bus stop. A soft and sooty cannonball at the time, he was kittenish but never outwardly friendly or playful as the more fawning of the species can be. Why I was chosen I have never been able to analyse, unless his father was a ship's mouser and my rolling, clopping but certain gait aroused in him some irrational folk memory. I accepted him from the first, having paid the price before for investigation, and he has been since an almost permanent extension of my right shoulder, thus correcting to some extent the bias of the opposite crutch and roll. I say almost permanent because cats too are subject to the calls of nature. He has toilet-trained himself however, and allows me the punctilio of first go wherever we happen to be, possibly because I have removed from him the onus of preying. He could do this very well I am sure, although I admit to being partisan. The only time he lets me down is when I drink beer:apart from these occasions, which are infrequent from reasons of self-preservation, he keeps up remarkably with me, scarcely ever having to pretend politely. Of course, unneutered (real) toms are known to be prodigious.

I don't think the frequency of bedding has accelerated since his arrival in my post-pubescent world. What is different is the quality, both of subjects and of acts. In the immediate circle, of course, fame spread and previous relations have returned to experiment after vowing never to see me again, and have admitted an improvement on what was by no means amateur before. But strangers seem to be drawn by him too, so much so that I am in the happy position of having to refuse, and being able to distribute largesse among whole men. When I intimated earlier that he never leaves my shoulder, I meant just that. He descends only to allow removal of the clothing on my torso, and thereafter, with velvet but sure paws, he returns to his perch. The excitement is then threefold, you see.

Of course, we do not have to work. Each of us lives in the luxurious lap of whomsoever has taken our current fancy, and for the duration of that boarding — it is always we who decide on disembarkation — our pleasure in giving is selfishly altruistic since our hostess is much improved in health on what she was at our appearance.

There seems to be no end in sight. I shall reach fifty tomorrow, which anniversary has been the spur to this written reflection, and he is somewhere in his thirty-fourth year. Each of us is slightly larger in certain areas than he was say twenty years since, but energy and joie de vivre remain infectiously unimpaired. The only appurtenances which have required renewal have been the pedal studs on crutch and peg. Over the years, brass has given way to rubber, but this is a minor concession, I feel. In any case, the latter type neither slips on concrete nor requires to be polished.

The work I've done in a transcription of Glasgow speech, in this book as elsewhere, relies for its understanding on a familiarity with the different registers of that speech in the reader. In that sense it's specifically "local", though I've found that people in other parts of Scotland by and large seem to understand it on the page fairly easily.

I suppose, to put it simply, all I can say is that I've been more and more interested since I started writing, in exploring the actual speech-sounds I hear and use myself, for both humorous and serious purposes. In terms of the actual form of my work on the page, I've been influenced most by American poets such as William Carlos Williams and Robert Lax.

The eighth 'Unrelated Incident' here has been produced as a poster (blue print on a yellow background) by the Glasgow Print Studio; 'Granny's' was published in **Broadsheet**, 'Honest' was published in **Glasgow University Magazine** and broadcast on Radio Four (Scotland).

Tom Leonard

Unrelated Incidents

(1)

its thi lang-
wij a thi
guhtr thaht hi
said its thi
langwij a
thi guhtr

awright fur
funny stuff
ur
Stanley Bax-
ter ur but
luv n science
n thaht naw

thi langwij
a thi
intillect hi
said thi lang-
wij a thi intill-
ects Inglish

then whin thi
doors slid
oapn hi raised
his hat geen
mi a fare-
well nod flung
oot his right

fit boldly n
fell eight
storeys
doon thi
empty
lift-shaft

(2)

ifyi stull
huvny
wurkt oot
thi diff-
rince tween
yir eyes
n
yir ears;
- geez peace,
pal!

fyi stull
huvny
thoata lang-
wij izza
sound-system;
fyi huvny
hudda thingk
aboot thi dif-
frince tween
sound
n object n
symbol; well,
ma innocent
wee
friend - iz
god said ti
adam:

a doant kerr
fyi caw it
an apple
ur
an aippl -
jist leeit
alane!

(3)

```
this is thi
six a clock
news thi
man said n
thi reason
a talk wia
BBC accent
iz coz yi
widny wahnt
mi ti talk
aboot thi
trooth wia
voice lik
wanna yoo
scruff. if
a toktaboot
thi trooth
lik wanna yoo
scruff yi
widny thingk
it wuz troo.
jist wanna yoo
scruff tokn.
thirza right
way ti spell
ana right way
ti tok it. this
is me tokn yir
right way a
spellin. this
is ma trooth.
yooz doant no
thi trooth
yirsellz cawz
yi canny talk
right. this is
the six a clock
nyooz. belt up.
```

(4)

sittn guzz-
lin a can
a newcastle
brown wotchn
scotsport hum-
min thi furst
movement a
nielsens thurd
symphony - happy
iz larry yi
might say;

a wuz jist turn-
in ovir thi
possibility uv
oapnin anuthir
can whin thi
centre forward
picked up
a loose baw:
hi huddiz back
tay thi
right back iz
hi caught
it wayiz in-
step n jist
faintn this way
then this
way, hi turnd
n cracked it;
jist turnd n
cracked it;
aw nwan move-
ment; in ti
thi net.

(5)

at thi grand
theological
tennis match
bitween thi
orthodox awl
crocks n
thi
trendy all-
stars, a
rammy
irruptid whin
a yung
trendy bov-
vir boy tellt
hiz mate
who hid an awl
crock scarf
roon hiz shoodirz,
thit he wuz in
a flaigrint
state uv
non-being-fur-
uthirz; tay
which thi
awl crock rep-
lied, why doant
yi shut yir
trap n wotch
thi gemm in
peace; its no
a gemm, hiz
trendy frend
replied,
naithur um a
wotchn it;
a um here ti
witness a
persn-ti-persn
encounter, bi-
fore thi umpire
iz meaninful
symbol,

fur thi umpire-
abuv-thi-
umpire; tay
which thi awl
crock replied:
thaht izza
loada pish.

mirabile dictu,
it startid
pishn; and in
thi troo spirit
a christian
bruthirhood, thi
pair sat miz-
zribly wotchn
thi empty
court,
undir thi wan
umbrella.

(6)

its aw thi
fault a
thi unions hi
said n thi
wurkirs beein
too greedy
hi added n
thi commies n
no inuff
moderates stonnin
upn gettin
coontid n
lame ducks gitn
whut huvyi
bailt oot n
white elifints
getn selt doon
thi river n
a mean
wiv goat tay
puhll in
wur belts n
wur bax ur
tay thi waw
yiv goat tay
admit it.

then hi took
ootiz nummer
eight n
geen a luvvly
wee chip up
right
biside thi flag
n tapptit doon
furra three:

a burdie.

(7)

dispite
thi fact
thit
hi bilonged
tay a
class uv
people
thit hid
hid thir
langwij
sneered
it
since hi
wuz born;

dispite
a long
history uv
poverty n
thi
violence uv
people in
positions
uv
power telln
him his
culture wuz
a sign
of his
inferiority;

thit fur
thi
purposes uv
cultural
statistics hi
didny really
exist; amaz-

in iz it
might seem
this
ordinary wurkn

man got
up wan day
n
wuz herd
tay rimark
thit

it wuzny
sitcha
bad day
tay be
alive

(8)

· in the beginning was the word
in thi beginning was thi wurd
in thi beginnin was thi wurd
in thi biginnin was thi wurd
in thi biginnin wuz thi wurd
n thi biginnin wuz thi wurd
nthi biginnin wuzthi wurd
nthibiginnin wuzthiwurd
nthibiginninwuzthiwurd
. in the beginning was the sound .

(9)

ahl jist cut up
   stairz furra quiet
     smoke a thoat whin

away it fleez
   lik a bullet oota
     gun roon thi nix

coarnir two wheelz
   na prerr right doon
     bath street yid thingk

it wuz Li Mong
   me hingin oan hoff
     wey up thi stairz

n jist whin ahd
   hawld masell thangk
     god tay thi tap step

then bang. oan goes
   thi brakes n ahm sent
     heed furst right doon

thi tap deck. ah jist
   flung masell na seat
     whin nix thing hi crawlz

alang thi road ziff
   thirwiz aw thi time nthi
     wurld. ahd bin quickir wokn.

Granny's

I bought today
an unbashed tin of
potato and leek soup and

sat watching its almost
perfectly cylindrical brightly
coloured shape quite
astonished while

Wagner's Flying Dutchman
played on the radio and
my 16 month old son
played with his
plastic bricks

Honest

A canny even remembir thi furst thing a remembir. Whit a
mean iz, a remembir aboot four hunner thingz, awit wance.
Trouble iz tay, a remembir thim aw thi time.

A thinka must be gon aff ma nut. Av ey thoat that
though — leasta always seemti be thinkin, either am jist
aboot ti go aff ma nut, or else am already affit. But yi ey
think, ach well, wance yir aff yir nut, yill no no yiraffit. But
am no so sure. A wish a wuz.

Even jist sitn doonin writn. A ey useti think, whenever a
felt like writn sumhm, that that wiz awright, aw yi hud to
say wuz, ach well, a think ahl sit doonin write sumhm, nyi
jiss sat doonin wrote it. But no noo, naw. A canny even day
that for five minutes, but ahl sitnlookit thi thing, nthink,
here, sumdayz wrote that afore. Then ahl go, hawlin aw thi
books oootma cupboard, trynti find out hooit wuz. Nwhither
a find out or no, it takes me that long luknfurit, a canny be
bothird writn any mair, wance av stoapt. An anyway, a tend
ti think, if it's wan a they thingz that might uv been writn
before, there's no much point in writin it again, even if
naibdy actually huz, is there?

It's annoyin — a feel av got this big story buldn up
inside me, n ivri day ahl sit down, good, here it comes, only
it dizny come at all. Nthi thing iz, it's Noah's if a even no
what thi story's goany be about, coz a doant. So a thinkty
ma cell, jist invent sumdy, write a story about a fisherman
or sumhm. But thi longer a think, thi mair a realise a canny
be bothird writn aboota fisherman. Whut wid a wahnti write
about a fisherman fur? N am no gonny go downti thi library,
nsay, huvyi enny booksn fishermen, jiss so's a can go nread
up about thim, then go n write another wan. Hoo wahntsti
read a story about fishermen anyway, apart fray people that
wid read it, so's they could go n write another wan, or
fishermen that read? A suppose right enough, thi trick
might be, that yi cin write a story about a fisherman, so long
as thi main thing iz, that thi bloke izny a fisherman, but a
man that fishes. Or maybe that izny right at all, a widny no.
But a do no, that as soon as a lookt up thi map ti see what
might be a good name furra fishn village, nthen maybe
went a walk ti think up a good name for a fisherman's boat,
nthen a sat nworked out what age thi fisherman should be,
nhow tall he wuz, nwhat colour his oilskins were, nthen

gotim wokn iniz oilskins, doon frae thi village tay iz boat, ad
tend ti think, whut duzzy wahnti day that fur? Kinni no day
sumhm else wayiz time? Aniffa didny think that ti masell, if
a jiss letm go, ach well, it's iz job, away out ti sea, ana big
storm in chapter two, ahd tend ti think, either, here, sumdyz
wrote that before, or, can a no day sumhm else wi ma time?
An in fact, if a came across sumdy sitn readn it eftir a did
write it, if a hud, ad tend ti thinkty ma cell, huv they got
nuthn behtr ti day wi their time?

    A don't no that am sayn whut a mean. But a suppose
underneath everythin, thi only person a want ti write about,
iz me. It's about time a wrote sumhm aboot masell! But
whut? Ah thought even, ach well, jist write doon a lohta yir
memories, then maybe they'll take some kinda shape, anyi
kin use that ti write a story wi, or a play, or a poem, or a
film-script, or God only knows whut, on thi fly. So that's
whuta did. Didny mahtr thi order, jist day eftir day, writn
doon ma memories. N ad be busy writn it, thinkin, whut an
incredible life av hud, even upti noo. Then ad be thinkin,
they'll no believe aw this hapnd ti me. Then a looktitit,
najistaboot threw up. It wiz nuthin ti day wi me at all. Nthi
other people ad be writin about, thi people ad met an that,
it wuz nuthin ti day wi them either. It might eveniv been
awright, if you coulda said it was about me nthem meetin.
but you couldny even say that. It wiz jis a lohta flamin
words.

    But that's sumhm else. Yi write doon a wurd, nyi sayti
yirsell, that's no thi way a say it. Nif yi tryti write it doon thi
way yi say it, yi end up wi thi page covered in letters stuck
thigithir, nwee dots above hof thi letters, in fact, yi end up
wi wanna they thingz yid needti huv took a course in
phonetics ti be able ti read. But that's no thi way a think, as
if ad took a course in phonetics. A doant mean that emdy
that's done phonetics canny think right — it's no a
questiona right or wrong. But ifyi write down "doon" wan
minute, nwrite doon "down" thi nixt, people say yir beein
inconsistent. But ifyi sayti sumdy, "Whaira yi affi?" nthey
say, "Whut?" nyou say, "Where are you off to?" they don't
say, "That's no whutyi said thi furst time." They'll probably
say sumhm lika, "Doon thi road!" anif you say, "What?" they
usually say, "Down the road!" the second time — though no
always. Course, they never really say, "Doon thi road!" or
"Down the road!" at all. Least, they never say it the way it's
spelt. Coz it izny spelt, when they say it, is it?

    A fine point, perhaps. Or maybe it izny, a widny no. Or

maybe a think it is, but a also a think that if a say, "Maybe it
izny" then you'll turn it over in your head without thinkin,
"Who does he think he is — a linguistic philosopher?" Or
maybe a widny bothir ma rump whether it's a fine point or it
izny: maybe a jist said it fur effect in thi furst place. Coz
that's sumhm that's dawned on me, though it's maybe
wanna they thingz that yir no supposed ti say. An thirz a
helluv a lohta them, when yi think about it, int thir? But
anyway, what's dawned on me, or maybe it's jist emergin
fray ma subconscious, is, that maybe a write jist tay attract
attention ti ma cell. An that's a pretty horrible thought ti
emerge fray emdy's subconscious, coz thi nixt thing that
emerges is, "Whut um a — a social inadequate?" N as if that
izny bad enough, thi nixt thing that yi find yirself thinkin, is,
"Am a compensatin for ma social inadequacy, 'by proxy', as
it were?" An thi nixt thing, thi fourth thing, that yi find
yirself thinkin, is, "If av committed maself, unwittinglv. ti
compensation 'by proxy', does that mean that a sense a
inadequacy, unwittingly, huz become a necessity?" An thi
fifth, an thi sixth, an thi seventh thingz that yi find yirself
thinkin, are, "Whut if ma compensation 'by proxy' is found
socially inadequate?" and "Ivdi's against me — a always
knew it," and "Perhaps posterity will have better sense."

"Thi apprentice has lifted ma balls an cock," said the
plumber. Sorry, that comes later. Am no sayin that these
seven thoughts necessarily come in the order in which av
presented thim. Ti some people, ahl menshin nay names,
these thoughts never emerge fray thir subconscious,
particularly thi fifth, which is, yi can imagine, thi most
terrible thought, of thi lot. Often it turns out that thoughts
six and seven are thi most popular, though thoughts one ti
five are largely ignored. But thi more yi ignore thoughts one
ti five, thi more thoughts six and seven will out. Coz
although thought five, "Whut if ma compensation 'by proxy'
is found socially inadequate?" never emerges fray yir
subconscious, there comes a day when, in a casual
discussion about Literature in general, sumdy says, "Your
stuff's a lohta rubbish." It might not even be so blunt — in
fact, what usually happens is, that in the foyer of a theatre
or sumhm, an in thi middle of a casual conversation about
Literature in general, then sumdy introduces you ti sumdy
else, an thi other person says, "Who?" An although "Who?"
might no sound like a literal translation of, "Your stuff's a
lohta rubbish," nonetheless, in the thoughts of a social
inadequate, it's as near as dammit. So havin secretly thunk

thought six, "Ivdi's against me — a always knew it," yi hurry
hame ti write sumhm, ti get yir ain back. These ur thi
symptoms. Coz yir that fed up wi ivdi yi know, so yi think,
that writin sumhm seems about thi only thing worth dayin.
Then at least when yir finished yi feel a hell of a lot better,
coz whoever it was that was gettin onyir wick before, yi can
go upty an say, "A don't gee a damn whut you think about
me, coz av jist wrote a poem, an that's sumhm you huvny
done. An even if yi huv, albetyi it wuz rotten." Course you
don't actually say all that — you don't huvti say it, even if yi
could be bothered. An if it's sumdy that did say ti you, "Your
stuff's a lohta rubbish," thirz no much point in goin upti thim
anyway, is there? But yi can ey jist look thim in thi eye, in
yir mind's eye, an think, "Perhaps posterity will have better
sense."

   "Ahma writur, your only a wurkur", a said , to thi
plumbir.

   "Fux sake Joe stick wan on that kunt," said the
apprentice.

   "Ball an cocks," said the plumber, "Ball an cocks. A
firgot ma grammur."

   "Gerrihtuppyi," a said, to thi apprentice.

   "Lissn pal yoor tea'll be up na minit," said the plumber.

   "Couldny fuckin write a bookie's line ya basturdn
illiturate," a said, ti the plumber.

   "Right. Ootside," said the plumber. "Mawn. Ootside."
   Sorry. That comes later.

I was born and bred in Glasgow
I have lived most of my life in Glasgow
It is the place I know best
My language is English
I write
In my writings the accent is in Glasgow
I am always from Glasgow and I speak English always
Always with this Glasgow accent

This is right enough

'Fifty Pence' has appeared in the York magazine **Eboracum,** and in the **Glasgow Review.** 'Remember Young Cecil' was included in **Scottish Short Stories 1975** and has also appeared in **Eboracum.**

'Where I was' is a short section from a far longer work which stuttered to a halt some months ago.

James Kelman

Remember Young Cecil?
he used to be a very Big Stick indeed

Young Cecil is medium sized and retired. For years he has been undisputed champion of our hall. Nowadays that is not saying much. This pitch has fallen from grace lately. John Moir who runs the place has started letting some of the punters rent a table Friday and Saturday nights to play Pontoons and as an old head pointed out the other day: that is it for any place, never mind Porter's.

In Young Cecil's day it had one of the best reputations in Glasgow. Not for its decoration or the rest of it. But for all round ability Porter's regulars took some beating. Back in they days we won the 'City' eight years running with Young Cecil Number 1 and Wee Danny backing up at Number 2. You could have picked any four from ten to make up the rest of the team. Between the two of them they took the lot three years running; snooker singles and doubles, and billiards the same. You never saw that done very often.

To let you know just how good we were, John Moir's big brother Tam could not even get into the team except if we were short though John Moir would look at you as if you were daft if you said it out loud. He used to make out Tam, Young Cecil and Wee Danny were the Big Three. Nonsense. One or two of us had to put a stop to that. We would have done it a hell of a lot sooner if Wee Danny was still living because young Cecil has a habit of not talking. All he does is smile. And that not very often either. I have seen Frankie Sweeney's boy come all the way down here just to say hello and what does Young Cecil do but give him a nod and at the most a how's it going without even a name nor nothing. But that was always his way and Frankie Sweeney's boy still drops in once or twice yet. The Big Noises remember Cecil. And some of the young ones. Tam? — never mind John Moir — Young Cecil could have gave Tam forty and potting only yellows still won looking round. How far!

Nowadays Young Cecil can hardly be annoyed even saying hello. But he was never ignorant. Always the same.

I mind fine the first time we clapped eyes on him. Years ago it was. In they days Young Cecil played up the Y.M. A hall's regulars kind of keep themselves to themselves but we still heard a young fellow from the Y.M. knew how to handle a stick. With a first name like Cecil nobody needed to know what his last one was. Wee Danny was Number 1 at the time. It is not so good as all that being Number 1 cause you have got to hand out big starts otherwise you are lucky to get anybody even to play you — never mind for a couple of bob. Of course there is always the one or two who do not mind losing a few bob because it does not matter just so long as they get a game with you.

Wee Danny was about twenty-seven or thirty in they days but no more than that. Well this afternoon we were just hanging about. None of us had a coin — at least not for playing with . During the week it was. A couple of us were knocking them about on table 3 which has always been the table in Porter's. Even John Moir would not dream of letting anybody mess about on that one. There were maybe three other tables in use at the time, but it was only mugs playing. Most of us were chatting or just studying form and sometimes one of us would carry a line up to Nicky at the top of the street. Well the door opened and in comes this young fellow. He walks up and stands beside us for a wee while. Then: Anybody fancy a game? he says. We all looks at one another and at Wee Danny in particular and then we bursts out laughing . None of you want a game then? he says.

Old Porter himself was running the place in they days. He was just leaning his elbows on the counter in his wee cubby-hole and sucking that falling-to-bits pipe of his. But he was all eyes in case of bother.

For a couple of bob? says the young fellow.

Well we all stopped laughing right away. I do not think Wee Danny had been laughing at all. He was just sitting up on the ledge dangling his feet. It was quiet for a minute then Sammy Parker steps forward and says that he would give the young fellow a game. Sammy was playing 4 stick at that time and hitting not a bad ball. But the young fellow just looks him up and down. Sammy was a big fat kind of fellow.

No: says the young one. He looks round at the rest of us but before he can open his mouth Wee Danny is off the ledge and smartly across.

You Young Cecil from the Y.M.?

Aye: says the young fellow.

Well I'm Danny Thompson. How much you wanting to play for?

Fiver.

Very good: Wee Danny turns and shouts: William!

Old Porter ducks below the counter and comes up with Danny's jar. Wee Danny always used to keep his money in a jam-jar in they days. And he had a good few quid in there at times. Right enough sometimes he had nothing.

Young Cecil took out two singles, a half quid and made the rest up with a pile of smash. He puts it on the shade above table 3 and Wee Danny done the same with his five singles. Old Porter went over to where the mugs were playing and told them to get a move on. One or two of us were a bit put out with Wee Danny because usually when there was a game on we got into it ourselves for a couple of bob. Sometimes with the other fellow's cronies and if there was none of them Wee Danny would maybe just cover half himself and let us make up the rest. Once or twice I have seen Wee Danny skint and having to play a money game for us. When he won we all chipped in and gave him his wages. Sometimes he liked the yellow stuff too much and when he got a right turn off he might go and you would be lucky to see him before he had bevied the lot. His money right enough — but he had to look to us a few times once he had done his all in so you might have thought: Okay I'll take three quid and let the lads get a bet with the deuce that's left. But no. Sometimes you were not too sure where you stood with Wee Danny. I have seen him giving some poor bastard a right sherricking for nothing any of us knew about. Aye, more than once. Not everybody liked him.

Meanwhile we were all settled along the ledge. Old Porter and Sammy were giving the table a brush. Wee Danny fiddled about with his cue but Young Cecil was just hanging about looking at the photos and shield and that, that Old Porter had hanging up in full view on the wall behind his counter. When they finished brushing the table Old Porter grumbles under his breath and goes over to the mugs who still had not ended their game. He tells them to fuck off and take up bools or something then locks the door after them and pulls down the blinds. He went back to his cubby-hole and brought out his chair so he could have a sit down to watch the game.

Sammy was marker. He chips the coin. Young Cecil calls right and breaks without a word. Well maybe he was a bit nervous, I do not know, but he made a right mess of it. His cue ball hit the blue after disturbing quite a few reds out the pack on its way up. Nobody could give Wee Danny a chance like that and expect him to stand back admiring

the scenery. He stepped right in and bump bump bump — a
break of fifty-six. One of the best he ever had. It was the
best of three they were playing. Some of us were looking
daggers at Danny for not letting us into it, not every day you
got a fiver bet. Wee Danny broke for the next and left a
good safety. But the young one had got over whatever it was
and his safety game was always good. It was close but
Young Cecil took that one. A rare game. Then he broke for
the decider and this time it was no contest . I have seen him
play as well but I do not remember him playing better. And
he was barely turned twenty at the time. He went right to
town and Wee Danny wound up chucking it on the colours
and you never saw that very often.

William: says Wee Danny and he gets the rest of the
cash out of his jar. He says to young Cecil: Same again son.

Double or clear if you like: says the young one.

Well Wee Danny never had the full tenner in his jar so
the rest of us dived into Old Porter for a couple of bob till
broo day and made up the bet because to tell the truth we
thought it was a bit of a flash-in-the-pan. And even yet
when I think about it you cannot blame us. They young
fellows come and go. Even now. They do not change. Still
think they are wide. Soon as they can pot a ball they are
ready to hand out J.D. himself three blacks of a start. Throw
their money at you. Usually we were there to take it and we
never had to call on Wee Danny much either. So how were
we supposed to know it was going to be any different this
time?

Sammy racked them and Young Cecil won the toss
again. He broke and this time left the cue ball nudging the
brown's arse. Perfect. Then on it was a procession. And he
was not just a potter like most of they young ones. Course at
that time it was his main thing just like the rest but the real
difference was young Cecil never missed the easy ones.
Never. He could take a chance like anybody else but you
never saw him miss the easy pot. One or two of us thought it
might not be a flash-in-the-pan but still fancied Wee Danny
to do the business because whatever else he was Wee
Danny was a money player. Some fellows are World Beaters
till there is a bet bigger than the price of renting the table
then that is them — all fingers and thumbs and miscueing
all over the shop. I have seen it many a time. And after
Young Cecil had messed his break in the first frame Wee
Danny had stepped in with his good score so we knew he
was on his game. Also the old heads reckoned Cecil might

crack up with the tenner bet plus the fact we were all into it
as well. Because Wee Danny could pot a ball with a
headcase at his back all ready to set about his head with a
hatchet if he missed. Nothing could put the wee man off his
game.

But he met his match that day.

He did not ask Young Cecil for another double or clear
either. In fact a while after the event I heard he never even
fancied himself for the second game — just felt he had to
play it for some reason.

After that Young Cecil moved into Porter's and ever
since it has been home. Him and Wee Danny got on well
enough but they were never close friends or anything like
that. Outside they went about in different crowds. There
was an age gap between them right enough. That might
have had something to do with it. And Cecil never went in
for the bevy the way the wee man did. In some ways he was
more into the game than Wee Danny was. Could work up an
interest even if there was no money involved whereas Wee
Danny was the other way.

Of course after Young Cecil met his he could hardly be
annoyed playing the game at all.

But that happened a while after — when we were
having the long run in the 'City'. Cleaning up everywhere
we were. And one or two of us were making a nice few bob
on the side. When Cecil left the Y.M. and started coming in
regular Wee Danny moved down to Number 2 stick and
within a couple of years people started hearing about
Young Cecil. But even then Wee Danny was making a good
few bob more than him because when he was skint Wee
Danny used to run about different pitches and sometimes
one or two of us went along with him and picked up a
couple of bob here and there. Aye and a few times he
landed us in bother because in some of they places it never
made any difference Wee Danny was Wee Danny. In fact
usually it just made it worse if they found out. He was hell of
a lucky not to get a right good hiding a couple of times. Him
and young Cecil never played each other again for serious
money. Sometimes they had an exhibition or that for maybe
a nicker or two to make it look good for the mugs but they
both knew who the 1 stick was and it never changed. That
might have been another reason for them not being close
friends or anything like that.

Round about then Young Cecil started playing in a
private club up the town where Wee Danny had played

once or twice but not very often. This was McGinley's place. The big money used to change hands there. Frankie Sweeney was on his way up then and hung about the place with the Frenchman and one or two others. Young Cecil made his mark right away and a wee bit of a change came over him. But that was for the best as far as we were concerned because up till then he was just too quiet. Would not push himself or that. Then all of a sudden we did not have to tell him he was Young Cecil. He knew it himself. Not that he went about shouting it out because he never did that at any time. Not like some of them you see nicking about all gallus and sticking the chest out at you. Young Cecil was never like that and come to think of it neither was Wee Danny though he always knew he was Wee Danny right enough. But now when Young Cecil talked to the one or two of us he did speak to it was him did the talking and we did not have to tell him.

Then I mind fine we were all sitting about having a couple of pints in the Crown and there at the other end of the bar was our 1 and 2 sticks. Now they often had a drink together before but normally it was always in other company. Never like this — by themselves right through till closing time. Something happened. Whenever Young Cecil went up to McGinley's after that Wee Danny always went with him as if he was partners or something. And they started winning a few quid. So did Sweeney and the Frenchman, they won a hell of a lot more. They two were on to Young Cecil from the early days.

Once or twice a couple of us got let into the club as well. McGinley's place was not like a hall. It was the basement in an office building up near George Square but it was a fairsized pitch though there was only the one table. It was set aside in a room by itself with plenty of seats round about it, some of them built up so everbody could see. The other room was a big one and had a wee bar and a place for snacks and that, with some card tables dotted about and there was a big table for Chemmy. None of your Pontoons up there. I heard talk about a speaker wired up for commentaries and betting shows and that but I never saw it myself. Right enough I was never there during the day. The snooker room was kept shut all the time except if they were playing or cleaning the place out. They kept it well.

McGinley and them used to bring players through from Edinburgh and one or two up from England to play exhibitions and sometimes they would set up a big match

and the money changing hands was something to see.
Young Cecil told us there were Glasgow fellows down there
hardly anybody had heard about who could really handle a
stick. It was a right eye-opener for him because up till then
he only know about people like Joe Hutchinson and
Simpson and one or two others who went in for the 'Scottish'
regular yet down in McGinley's there were two fellows
playing who could hand out starts to the likes of Simpson.
Any day of the week. It was just that about money players
and the rest.

So Young Cecil became a McGinley man and it was not
long before he joined Jimmy Brown and Sandy from
Dumfries in taking on the Big Sticks through from
Edinburgh and England and that.

Then Sweeney and the Frenchmen set up a big match
with Cecil and Jimmy Brown. And Cecil beat him. Beat him
well. A couple of us were let in that night and we picked up
a nice wage because Jimmy Brown had been around a good
while and had a fair support. In a way it was the same story
as Cecil and Wee Danny only this time Wee Danny and the
rest of Porter's squad had our money down the right way
and we were carrying a fair wad for some of us who were not
let in. There was a good crowd watching because word
travels but it was not too bad because McGinley was hell of
a strict about letting people in — in case it put the players
off in any way. With just onlookers sitting on the seats and
him and one or two others standing keeping an eye on
things it usually went well and you did not see much funny
business though you heard stories about one or two people
who tried it on at one time or another. But if you ask me any
man who tried to pull a stroke down McGinley's was
needing his head examined.

So Young Cecil wound up the man in Glasgow they all
had to beat, and it was a major upset when anybody did.
Sometimes when the likes of Hutchinson came through we
saw a fair battle but when the big money was laid down it
was never on top of him if he was meeting Young Cecil.
Trouble was you could hardly get a bet on Cecil less he was
handing out starts. And then it was not easy to find a punter
and even when you could there was liable to be upsets
because of the handicapping.

But it was good at the time. Porter's was always buzzing
cause Young Cecil was still playing 1 with Wee Danny at
Number 2. It was rare to walk into an away game knowing
everybody was waiting for Young Cecil and Porter's to

arrive and the bevy used to flow. They were good days and
one or two of us could afford to let our broo money lie over a
week if we wanted though none of us ever did. Obviously.
Down in McGinley's we were seeing some rare tussles.
Young Cecil was not always involved but since he was
Number 1 more often than not he was in there somewhere at
the wind up.

It went well for a hell of a long while.

Then word went the rounds that McGinley and
Sweeney and one or two others were bringing up Cuddihy.
He was known as the County Durham at that time. Well
nobody could wait for the day. It was not often you got the
chance of seeing Cuddihy in action and when you did it was
worth going a long way to see. He liked a punt and you
want to see some of the bets he used to make at times — on
individual shots and the rest of it. He might be about to pot
a long difficult one and then just before he lets fly he stands
back from the table and cries: Okay who'll lay me six to four
to a couple of quid?

And sometimes a mug would maybe lay him thirty
pound to twenty. That is right, that was his style. A bit
gallus but he was pure class. And he could take a good
drink. Hell of a man. To be honest even us in Porter's did not
fancy Young Cecil for this one — and that includes Wee
Danny. They said the County Durham was second only to
the J.D. fellow though I never heard of them meeting
seriously together. But I do not go along with them that said
the J.D. fellow would have turned out second best if they
ever had. But we will never know.

They were saying it would be the best game ever seen
in Glasgow and that is something. All the daft rumours
about it being staged in a football ground were going the
rounds. That was nonsense. Pure rubbish. McGinley was a
shrewdie and if he wanted he could have put it on at the
Kelvin Hall or something but the game took place in his
club and as far as everybody was concerned that was the
way it should be even though most of us from Porter's could
not get in to see it at the death.

When the night did finally come it was like an Old Firm
game on New Year's Day. There was more people in the
card room than actually let in to see the game and in a way
it was not right, for some of the ones left out were McGinley
regulars and they had been turned away to let in people we
had never seen before. And some of us were not even let
into the club at all. Right enough some of us had never been

to McGinley's before, just went to Porter's and thought that
would do. So they could not grumble. But one or two of us
who would have been down in McGinley's every night of the
week if they had let us were classed as I do not know what
and not let in. So that was not fair. Even Wee Danny was
lucky to get watching as he told us after. He was carrying
our money. And there was some size of a wad there.
Everybody who ever set foot in Porter's was on to Cecil that
night. And some from down our way who never set foot in a
snooker hall in their life were on him as well and you cannot
blame them. The pawn shops ran riot. Everything hockable
was hocked just to get a bet on Young Cecil. We all went
daft. But there was no panic about not finding a punter
because everybody knew that Cuddihy would back himself
to his last penny. Hell of a man. Aye and he was worth a
right few quid as well. Wee Danny told us just before the
marker chipped the coin Cuddihy stepped back and shouts:
Anybody still wanting a bet now's the time!

And there was still takers even at that minute. All right,
we all knew how good the County Durham was but it made
no difference because everybody thought he had made a
right bloomer. Like Young Cecil said to us when the news
broke a week before the contest: Nobody, he says, can give
me that sort of start. I mean it. Not even J.D. himself.

And we believed him. We agreed with him. It was
impossible. That any man alive could give Young Cecil
thirty of a start in each of a five-frame match sounded
ridiculous to our way of thinking. Wee Danny was the same.

Off of thirty I'd play him for everything I've got. I'd lay
my weans on it. No danger! He says: Cuddihy's coming the
cunt with us. Young Cecil'll sort him out proper. No danger!

And that was the way of it as far as everybody else was
concerned. Right enough on the day you got the one or two
who bet the County Durham. Maybe they had seen him play
and that, or heard about him and the rest of it. But
reputations are made to be broke and apart from that one or
two and Cuddihy and his mates everybody else was on to
Cecil. And they thought they were stonewall certainties!

How wrong we all were.

Yet what can you say? Young Cecil played well. After
the event he said he could not have played much better.
Just that the County Durham was in a different class. His
exact words. What a turn-up for the books. Cuddihy won the
first two frames then Young Cecil got a chance in the next
but Cuddihy came again and took the fourth for the best of
five. Easy. Easy.

What can you do? Wee Danny told us the Frenchman called Young Cecil a good handicapper and nothing else.

Well that was that and a hell of a lot of long faces were going about our side of the river — Porter's was like a cemetery for ages after it. Some of the old heads say it's been going downhill ever since. I do not know. Young Cecil was the best we ever had. Old Porter said there was none better in his day either. So what do you do? Sweeney told Young Cecil it was no use comparing himself with the likes of Cuddihy but you could see it did not matter.

Young Cecil changed overnight. He got married just before the game anyway so what with that and the rest he dropped off a bit. He still played 1 stick for us right enough and had the odd game down McGinley's once or twice but slowly and surely he just dropped away out of things and then somebody spoke for him in Fairfield's and he wound up getting a start in there as a docker or something. But after he retired he started coming in regular again. Usually he plays billiards nowadays with the one or two of us that are still around. Mind you he is still awful good.

No Longer the Warehouseman

What matters is that I can no longer take gainful employment. That she understands does not mean I am acting correctly. After all — one's family must eat and wear clothes, be kept warm in the winter and they must also view television if they wish — like any other family. To enable all of this to come to pass I must earn money. Thirteen months have passed. This morning I had to begin a job of work in a warehouse as a warehouseman. My year on the labour exchange is up — was up? I am unsure at the moment. No more money was forthcoming unless I had applied for national assistance which I can do but dislike doing for various reasons.

I am worried. A worried father. I have two children, a wife, a stiff rent, the normal debts. To live I should be working but I cannot. This morning I began a new job. As a warehouseman. My wife will be sorry to hear I am no longer gainfully employed in the warehouse. My children are of tender years and will therefore be glad to see me once more about the house although I have only been gone since breakfast time and it is barely five o'clock in the afternoon so they will scarcely have missed me. But my wife: This is a grave problem. One's wife is most understanding. This throws the responsibility onto one's own shoulders however. When I mention the fact of my no longer being the warehouseman she will be sympathetic. There is nothing to justify to her. She will agree with me. She will also take for granted that the little ones shall be provided for. Yet how do I accomplish this without the gainful employment. I do not know. I dislike applying to the social security office. On occasion one has in the past lost one's temper and deposited one's children on the counter and been obliged to shamefacedly return five minutes later in order to uplift them or accompany the officer to the station. I do not like the social security. Also one has difficulty in living on the money they provide.

And I must I must. Or else find a new job of work. But after this morning one feels one... well, one feels there is something wrong with one.

I wore a clean shirt this morning lest it was expected. Normally I dislike wearing shirts unless I am going to a dinner dance etcetera with the wife. No one was wearing a shirt but myself and the foreman. I did not mind. But I took off my tie immediately and unbuttoned the top two buttons. They gave me a fawn dusk or dust perhaps coat, to put on — without pockets. I said to the foreman it seemed ridiculous to wear an overcoat without pockets. And also I smoke so require a place to keep cigarettes and the box of matches. My trousers pockets are useless. My waist is now larger than when I aquired these particular trousers. Anything bulky in their pockets will cause a certain discomfort.

One feels as though one is going daft. I should have gone straight to the labour exchange and told the clerk some tale or other. I cannot even lie apparently. And possibly said... what. I do not know. I have not even collected my insurance cards from the warehouse office. Nor receipt.

I am not going to receive any money. I have to go to the social security in order to get money. Firstly I must sign on at the labour exchange and get a new card and then go to the social security office. I shall take my B1 and my rent book and stuff, and stay calm at all times. They shall make an appointment for me and I shall be there on time otherwise they will not see me. My nerves get frayed. My wife knows little about this. I tell her next to nothing but at other times tell her everything.

I do not feel like telling my wife I am no longer the warehouseman and that next Friday I shall not receive the sum of twenty five pounds we had been expecting. A small wage. I told the foreman the wage was particularly small. Possibly his eyes clouded. I was of course cool, polite. This is barely a living wage I told him. Wage. An odd word. But I admit to being aware of all this when I left the labour exchange to commence employment there. Nobody diddled me. My mind was simply blank. My year was up. One year and six weeks. I could have stayed unemployed and been relatively content. But for the social security. I did not wish to risk losing my temper. Now I shall just have to control myself. Maybe send the wife. This might be the practical solution. And the clerks shall look more favourably upon one's wife. Perhaps increase one's rate of payment.

I found the job on my own. Through the evening times sits vac col. It was a queer experience using the timecard once more. Ding ding as it stamps the time. I was given a knife along with the overcoat. For snipping string.

I am at a loss. I may in reality be losing my reason. At
my age and considering my parental responsibilities, for
example my wife and two weans, I should be paid more
than twenty five pounds. I told the foreman this. It is a start
he replied. Start fuck all I answered. It is the future which
worries me. How on earth do I pay the monthly rent of
£34.30. My wife will be thinking to herself I should have
kept the job till securing another. It would have been
sensible. Yes. It would have been sensible. Right enough. I
cannot recall why I accepted the job in the first instance. I
actually wrote a letter in order to secure an interview. At
the interview I was of course cool, polite. Explained that my
wife had been ill this past thirteen months. I was most
interested in the additional news, that of occasional
promotional opportunities. Plus yearly increments and cost
of living naturally. Word for word. One is out of touch at the
labour exchange. I knew nothing of cost of living
allowance. Without which I would have been earning
twenty two sixty or thereabouts.

It is my fault. My wife is to be forgiven if she… what.
She will not do anything.

There were five other warehousemen plus three
warehouselads, a forkliftdriver, the foreman and myself. At
teabreak we sat between racks. An older chap sat on the
floor to stretch his legs. Surely there are chairs I said to the
foreman.

Once the owner had downed his tea I was handed his
cup which had astonishing chips out of it. It was kind f him
but I did not enjoy it. And I do not take sugar. But it cost
nothing. Once I receive my wages I am to pay twenty five
pence weekly. I should not have to pay for sugar. It does not
matter now.

Time passes. My children age. My wife is in many ways
younger than me. She will not say a word about all this. One
is in deep trouble. One's bank account lacks money
enough. I received a sum for this morning's work but it will
shortly be spent. Tomorrow it is necessary I return to the
labour exchange. No one will realise I have been gone. No
one knows me anyway. That is not true. I nod to certain
among them. Next week should be better. If this day could
be wiped from my life, or at least go unrecorded, I would be
happy.

The warehousemen were discussing last night's
television. I said good god.

A funny smell . A bit musty. Soggy cardboard perhaps.

The boss, the boss, not the foreman, is called Mister Jackson. The foreman is called George. The problem is I can no longer. Even while climbing the subway stairs; as I left the house; was eating my breakfast; rose from bed; watched television last night: I expected it would prove difficult.

Mister Jackson is the boss. He also wears a shirt and tie. Later this morning the express carriers arrived and all of we warehousemen and lads were to heave to and load up. It is imperative we do so before lunch, said Mister Jackson. I have to leave, I said to him. Well hurry back, replied George. No. I mean I can no longer stay. I am going home, I explained. And could I have my insurance cards and money for this morning's work. What, cried Mister Jackson. George the foreman was blushing in front of Mister Jackson. Could I have my cards and money please, it is imperative I go for a pint and home to see the wife.

I was soon paid off although unable to get my insurance cards there and then.

The problem is of course the future — financing the rearing of one's offspring etcetera.

The City Slicker and the Barmaid

I came to someplace a few miles south of the Welsh border and with luck managed to rent a tent on a farm. Not a camping site. I was the one mug living on the dump and could only stay on condition I completed certain set tasks such as painting barn walls or driving tractors. And whenever the farmer was away on business I had to guide his ramshackle lorry into the village.

I also received cash for these tasks.

The grass was long in the field where I had to pitch the tent. Closeby was a barn. Here big rats jumped about getting fat on the hay and feed stored inside. Sometimes I discovered paw marks on the grease in my frying pan. This proves the rats got into my tent though the farmer would never believe me. During the night I liked to sit at the top end of the tent with a bottle in one hand waiting for a thing to creep in. And the hedge surrounding this field was full of beetles and other flying insects. When I lit my candle they broke into the tent, waited on the roof till I was sleeping then came zooming down on me, eating my blood and knocking their knees in my hair. I was always waking in the middle of the night scratching and clawing at my scalp.

The actual farm animals themselves did not worry me. Although after sundown a pack of cows used to try and sniff me; they came wastling along at my back without a sound bar the shshsh of their smelly tails. And no comfort entering my tent with the boots soaked through with dew. I was obliged to take them off at the door, seated on the groundsheet with the tent flaps wide open. A terrible tent. Two inch walls and sagging everywhere. The kind of effort a scoutmaster buys at christmas for his six year old son. And the groundsheet was always covered in clumps of grass, earwigs and spiders. Dung too at times: I had thought my boots okay enough to come straight in. No sleeping bag. Terrible itchy ex-army blankets hired from the farmer's wife at thirty pence a week. Of course my feet stuck out at the bottom and I can never sleep wearing socks.

The farmhands were continually cracking jokes in Oi Bee accents at my expense. At times I would laugh, or stare — other times I replied in aggressive accents of my own which got me nowhere since they pretended not to

understand what I was saying. Because I drove the lorry I
was accorded a certain respect. In the local den of a pub I
was known as Jock the Driver. Their previous driver was an
Irishman who worked seven years on the farm till one
Saturday night he went out for a pish in the lavatory round
the back of the pub. It was the last they ever saw of him. A
man to admire. The men working beside me were yesmen to
the core. Carried tales about each other to the farmer and
even to me if the farmer was off on business. Whole days
spent gossiping. I never spoke to them unless I had to. The
tightest bunch of bastards I have ever met. Never share
their grub or mugs of tea. Or their cash if you are skint. And
they never offer you a cigarette. If you buy them a drink
they think you are off your head and also resent it because
they feel obliged to buy you one back. In their opinion city
folk are either thieves or simpletons. An amazing shower of
crackpots the lot of them.

The barmaid in this pub was a daughter of the village. I
think she must have hated me because I represented
outside youth. And apart from myself there were no other
single men of her age in the dump. She was chaste I think
unless the Irishman ever got there which I doubt. I never
fancied her in the first place. A bit tubby. Just that if I hadnt
tried I thought the regulars might have felt insulted — the
barmaid not good enough etcetera for a city slicker like me.
The night I made the attempt was awful. It reminds me of B
feature imitation Barbara Stanwyck films.

Once or twice the manager used to bolt his doors and
allow a few regulars to stay behind after closing time. He
must have forgotten about me. With the shutters drawn and
the local constable in the middle of his second pint of cider,
I for some reason threw an arm about the barmaid's waist
for which I was dealt an almighty clout on the jaw. What a
fist she had on her. I was so amazed I tried to land her one
back but missed and fell across the table where the
constable was sitting, knocking the drink over him. I was
ejected.

Long after midnight, maybe as late as two in the
morning, I came back to apologise if anyone was still about
and also to collect the carry-out I had planked in the grass
behind the lavatory. I had been wandering about retching
for ages because of that country wine they had been
feeding me. Powerful stuff. Inside the lights were dimmed
but I knew they were there. I could hear music coming
faintly from the lounge. I crept round the side of the

building then up on my toes and peering through the corner of the frosted glass I spied the barmaid there giving it a go as the stripper. Yes. Doing a strip show on top of the lounge bar watched by the copper, the manager and one or two regulars, including an unhealthy old guy called Albert Jenkinson who worked alongside me on the farm. And all silent while they watched. Not a smile among them. Even the drink was forgotten. Just the quick drag on the smoke.

I lost my temper at first then felt better, then again lost my temper and had to resist caving in the window and telling them to stick the countryside up their jacksie.

No one noticed me. I did not stay very long. Her body was far too dumpy for a stripper and her underwear was a bit old fashioned. Her father worked as a gardener in the local nursery and very rarely ever went into the pub.

Once I got my wages the following week, and it was safe, I got off my mark and took the tent with me.

Where I Was

At least I am elsewhere. A wind like the soundtrack from a North Pole documentary rages underneath. I have absconded from my former abode leaving neither note nor arrears. I left arrears, I left no cash to discharge them. No explanations of any kind. Simply: I am somewhere else. No persons who knew me then or in fact at any time know of my whereabouts. Season: Midwinter. Equipage: As listed but boots as opposed to others I may have worn previously. And also a leather pouch instead of my old tobacco tin. Jesus and also a piece of cloth resembling a tartan scarf.

There are no lights. I am resting having walked many miles. I am well wrapped up; brown paper secured round my chest by means of the scarf crossed and tucked inside my trousers, a couple of safety pins are in there somewhere too. My health has got to remain fine otherwise my condition will deteriorate. At present I do not even have a runny nose. I stopped here because of the view. No other reason, none, nothing. I look down between mainland and island. Both masses ending in sheer drops, glowering at each other, but neither quite so high as where I am though maybe they are. Miles separate us. How many, I would be guessing. Rain pours. Sky very grey. Truth is I cannot tell what colour the sky is. May not even be there for all I know. And I reckon it must be past ten o'clock. A car passed some time ago. A Ford it was but a big one. Expensive model. Below, the tide reaches up to the head of the loch. No islets visible. My boots are not leaking. I laid out six quid on them. In the glen at the head of the loch are houses; I see lights there, and also opposite where I am a big house can be seen—white during daylight I imagine. A large dwelling house. It looks far from safe. Surrounded by tall, bent trees. A cabin cruiser tethered to a narrow jetty. Apart from all this nothing of moment.

Back a distance sheep were nibbling weeds. I saw them from thirty yards and knew what they were immediately.

I left the room in Glasgow recently and got here before the Ford car. There is something good about all this I cannot explain away. Not only the exhilarating gale blowing the dirty scalp clean. Nor the renunciation of all debts relating to the past while. Maybe it is as simple.

From here the road twists, falls to a village where there has to be a pub. As pubs go it will be averagely not bad. I won't stop. The place will be closed anyway. This afternoon I slept in a public convenience. Clean, rarely used by the smell of it. I should have invested in a tent. Not at all — a good thick waterproof sleepingbag would have been sufficient. I am spending money as I go but have a deal of the stuff, enough to be without worries for sometime. If I find a rowing boat tied near the shore I might steal it and visit the island across the way. Unlikely. Dare say I could swim it. Deceptive gap perhaps no more than two miles. Drown. At one time it would have presented no problem. Never mind.

I enjoy this walking. Amble and race, set off trotting and once I ran pell mell for quite a stretch — till a tractor saw me. Take baby steps and giants steps and assume odd postures and if a car passes I shriek with laughter. Sing all songs. My jaw aches. My ears ache. Perhaps the wind clogs them. Noises in my head. Sound like a lunatic. But my nose remains dry. Probably impending bronchitis. Next time I waken with a bone dry throat I shall know for sure. When I become immune to the wind everything will be fine.

Well stocked up on tobacco, always carry cheese and whisky in case of emergencies; fever and that. The notion to buy a pipe. But I must be sure of smoking it. I have no room for useless piles of tobacco. I handrolled pipe tobacco in the past. Terrible stuff.

From Ardanruiach the road curves steeply through a glen owned by someone whose name escapes me. Stiff climb. Tired my knees in particular. For the eventual relief of walking with straight legs I firstly walked with bent ones, at the knees. Black specs in front or slightly above my eyes. The blood cannot be as good as the best. But the wind. I heard it all the time. Loud racket never dying. I thought of climbing a mountain. Rain is the real problem. Whenever it falls I am affected. Soaks in knocking my hearing out. I am unable to look upwards for any length of time. It is damaging my boots and perhaps my coat. If my hair is plastered down over my brow in too irritating a manner water will drip down my sleeve when I push it back up. Terrible sensation. Vehicles splash me. The face red raw, my nose must be purple, constant drip drip from either nostril. Beads hang onto my eyelashes, cling to my eyebrows, fall from my chin down my neck — from my hair at the back down my neck it streams down my spinal cord, gets rubbed and rubbed by my trouser waistband into the skin at the small of my back. And no respite for my hands inside the coat pockets. The sleeves of the coat are far too wide so only my flesh actually enters each pocket; the wet clothing irritates my wrists and tiny pools of water gather in the nylon pocket material. The rain spoils the walk but it brightens. Always brightens eventually. Then I see water on the leaves of bushes and I can skite a branch to see the beads drop. The road dries in patches, swiftly, sometimes I can sit on such a spot though not for long of course.

In the future I hope to sleep during the day regularly. Apparently people do sleep on their feet, the bastards. And I try striding with my eyes shut once I have noted the direction.

I enjoy night. Not dusk so much because I know pubs do business, possibly it gets easier when the days lengthen. I shall sleep all day perhaps. With this constant exercise four hours kip won't be enough. And I shall be swimming when the water heats. Eating does not worry me yet. My money will run out. My best sleep so far was had in a hostel closed for the winter. Very simple to enter. No food but I found plenty of firewood. It burned fine. I spread all of my clothes on the backs of chairs in front of the fire. And washed both pairs of socks and had a complete body wash which may not have been a good idea since two or three layers of old skin went down the drain. This explains why I am freezing. Unfortunately I am really particular about clean feet and socks. I dont bother about underwear, seldom have any. Up until the wash I was wearing each pair of socks on alternate days, I wore both when sleeping. They had a stale, damp smell. My feet were never wholly dry. Small particles stuck to the toejoints, the soles of the feet. I had to see it all every day when I made the change of socks. In future I shall steel myself if it means warmer feet. And may even take to wearing both pairs daily, in other words keep them on at all times. Christ I wont be surprised if I catch the flu. I have acted foolishly. No wonder tramps dont wash. Yet what happens when the summer comes and I want a swim.

I considered staying in the hostel indefinitely. Could have returned. It wont be forgotten. I was going to hang a sign of my own for other wayfarers explaining how easy it was to break and enter, but did not do it. The reason reflects badly on me.

This day was bitter. Never warm inside the coat. That fucking wind went through me. Tried everything from walking sideways to hiding behind trees. All I could finally do was stride along punching my boots hard down on the road with my shoulders rigid, hunched up. This induced prolonged shivering but was the best I could manage. Every part of me cold, sick cold. Now and then I stopped for a swig of the stuff.

When the road closed into the water again I cut off through the marsh and down to the edge of the loch or maybe it was the sea. There was land far out. An island? Amazing silence, nothing but the waves breaking, lapping in over the pebbles. Where I was the wind was forgotten. Almost warm. I took off my coat and used it as a cushion on a dry rock a little way back. No fishing boats. I saw only small birds, landbirds, the country equivalent to sparrows, I suppose. My mind got into a certain state. The usual blankness. A trance or something like it. Time obviously passed. Clear. I finished my whisky and chain smoked. Staying put. No wish to walk the shore in search of a better position. The rain came later. Fine drizzle, spotting the water. I watched on for a bit then had to put the coat across my shoulders and shelter beneath the trees. But I remained for quite a while. Might have pitched a tent there.

Fifty Pence

The old woman opened her eyes when the gas-light flickered, but soon closed them again. With the newspaper raised nearer his eyes the boy squinted at the football news on the back page, trying to find something new to read. He let the paper fall onto his lap and lifted the tongs. He released the catch and wangled the points round a large coal lying in the shovel and carefully placed it on the spare fire in the grate. The old woman regarded him gravely for a moment. When he smiled back her forehead wrinkled in a taut kindly expression. Her eyes roamed upwards to the clock then the lids closed over.

He glanced at the clock; 8.40. He should have been home by now. The poker lay near his foot inside the fire-surround. He wanted to rake among the ashes to see if anything red remained. Perhaps there would be enough to kindle the lump and save the fire, perhaps the new lump was too big to catch light. The rustle as he turned a page of the paper seemed to reverberate around the narrow, high ceilinged kitchen. There was nothing to keep him. His parents would be annoyed. The bus journey home took nearly an hour and during the long winter nights they liked him to be in bed by ten. They would guess he was here.

He got to his feet, stretched. The movement roused the old woman; she muttered vaguely about apples being in the cupboard. He drank a mouthful of water straight from the brass tap then returned to his chair.

The fire looked dead. Lifting the poker suddenly he dug right into the ashes. The old woman bent forward and took the poker from him without comment. Gripping it with her right hand she moved her left deftly in and out the coals. Finally she balanced the new lump on smaller pieces, her thin fingers indifferent to any heat which may have remained. The poker was put back in position; handle on the floor with its sooty point projected in the air, lying angled against the fender. Wiping her fingertips on her apron she walked to the door and through to the parlour.

Neither spoke when she came back. She sat on her wooden chair and stared into the fire. Cloying black smoke drifted from the new lump. It crackled.

A little after 9.45 she looked up on hearing the light rap

on the outside door. The boy stirred from his doze. He made
to rise and answer but relaxed when she indicated he
should remain where he was. The outside door opened and
closed, and muttering as the footsteps approached. She
came in first and he followed, he appeared to be limping
slightly. Mumbling incoherently and did not notice his
grandson. She moved across to the sink and filled the kettle
and set it on the oven gas to make a pot of tea. The boy
wondered if she knew what his grandfather was saying to
her. He called a greeting. The old man turned slowly and
stared at him. The boy grinned but the old man turned back
and resumed the muttering. His grandmother seemed to
notice nothing odd about it. As the old man spoke he was
scratching his head. There was no bunnet. The bunnet was
not on his head.

The muttering stopped, the old man stared at the
woman then at the boy. The boy looked helplessly at her but
she watched the man. The expression on her face gave
nothing away. Her usual face. Again the boy called a
greeting but the old man turned to her and continued his
muttering. The tone of his voice had altered now; it was
angry. She looked away from him. When her gaze fell on
him the boy tried to smile. He was aware that, if he blinked,
tears would appear in his eyes. He smiled at her.

Ten shillings I'm telling you, said the voice.

The boy and his grandmother looked quickly at the old
man.

Ten shillings, Frances, he said. The anger had gone
from his voice.

As if noticing the boy for the first time he looked
straight at him. For several seconds he stood watching the
boy then he turned sharply back to face his wife: Ach, he
grunted.

She was standing holding the apron bunched in her
fists. Shaking his head the man attempted a step towards
her but fell backwards to the floor. He sat there for a
moment then fell sideways. The boy ran across crying it was
okay — it was okay.

His grandmother spoke as he bent down over the old
man.

He fell down, she said. He fell down.

She knelt by him on the floor and together they tried to
raise him to his feet but it was difficult; he was heavy. The
boy dragged over a chair and they managed to get him up
onto it. He slumped there, his head lolling, his chin
touching his chest.

He lost money, said the old woman, he said he lost money. That was what kept him. He went looking the streets for it and lost his bunnet.

It's okay, Grannie, the boy said.

It kept him late, she said.

The boy asked if they should try and get him changed and into bed but she did not reply. He asked again, urgently.

I'll get him, son, she said eventually. You can get away home now.

He looked at her in surprise.

Your mum and dad will be wondering where you've got to, she added.

It was pointless saying anything more. He could tell that by her face. Crossing to the bed in the recess he lifted his coat and slipped it on. He opened the door. When he glanced back his grandmother nodded. She was grasping her husband by the shoulders, propping him up. He could see the old man looking at her. He could see the big bald patch on the head. His grandmother nodded once again. He left then.

Jim Dandy

My dwelling. The state of the dump six days on my own. Crockery. Old layers of cold scrambled eggs. Smells of the place. Smells of the bedclothes. Nothing tucked in .Tangled sheets not covering my feet. Naked, alone in here with ash lying by the ashtray, a spent match next to three books and an erotic one just below the bed. A neighbour perhaps may offer to clean the place before the wife gets back.

My woman; enough said.

So grateful I awaken to morning. And very early as usual after a drink. And the immediate need to urinate. Such an erection. Nothing at all but a scrimp of cheese whose wrapping paper alone turns me off. Black coffee. Knees drawn up, huddled before the electric fire. The uncomfortable heat. My trouser bottoms hanging then burning my skin when I sit back. On the second smoke with the same coffee I feel better though it is possible she will die in childbirth and I to rear the kid by myself.

The newsagent has me stay for tea which we sip munching chocolate biscuits. How will I manage to earn a living? The child being taken from me. Or me giving it away.

Back upstairs with the morning paper and for some reason I brush my teeth and follow up with a smooth shave. I dress for other people then later I have a bath in the public washhouse. Consider a haircut.

She is so pleased to see me: And looking so spruce. Proud of me in front of the other women. They see me as a man against their own. Mayby they dont. I nod to certain among them I recognise, also the husband three beds along who wants a boy if possible. The state of the dump cheers her up. She really wants to come home, I want that so much I dont speak. Neither of us thinks of returning a trio. On the bus home I think of that. And later I wander round to her mother's and borrow two quid and my dinner. And a couple of pints with Peter my father-in-law.

Good lassie Moira, he says. Bit like her mother in some ways but not too bad son. Always had her eye on you. Even when you were weans together. Aye. Me a grandpa as well.

Me a father.

Aye. Jesus Christ son. Hey Bertie. Stick a couple of

Castellas with that order eh. Aye and listen son. Dont let
Moira's maw upset you. She likes you well enough.

Ach I know that Peter.

Aye. Aye. Well. All the best son.

He gives me a fiver as we split, pushes it into my top
pocket, embarrassed. Claps my shoulder. He likes me and I
like him and his wife is alright. He knows that because me
and his daughter share a bed sex has to happen. Perhaps he
regrets all the dirty jokes with his workmates or something.

Back at the hospital nothing is doing. The feeling that
they were enjoying the female banter before we all arrived.
The looks from the staff. I am too sensitive. They are not
really men haters. If you see what they have to do. My
aggression once more. I shake her hand to leave but she
wakens me by demanding a kiss; it brings us together. Her
smell. She hates to see me walk out of the place. Turning
when I get to the door I glimpse her, small there, watching
me go. Fuck it. The protective male. Is what sickens the
nurses maybe. Apart from me. It is just a fact. I cannot
change. All that much.

In the local hangout a cloistered male group backs onto
me with the stupid jokes and the new office girls and the
quick glance to the door each time it bangs open. And the
girl in the mirror ordering two shandies. Hell of a crush: I
gasp to her. She half smiles in reply. My stupid face in the
mirror. I have to get out of this bar and subway to the
Cross. Sometime since I last came this way but the crowd
are pleased to see me and I explain the past while. Soon drunk
and bouts of gabbing followed by blank silences.

On the road to somebody's house I let my legs wobble,
confide to the one supporting me that it's like this man.
Though I know it comes to everybody all the time I cant
help... The bastards in their spikinspan clothes. The shit in
the back close. The tea soaked newspaper hanging out the
dustbin. The smelly black stuff puddling between the
midden and the back close with bits of I dont know what
floating about and dog gangs following the bitch in their
maze and.

But later I feel better — even to shouting: Dont worry
about me. Jim Dandy. Just what the doctor etceterad. When
I overheard someone saying they should not have brought
me.

The wives and girlfriends waiting for us. I slump in a
chair glad to be breathing, even begin an occasional
conversation. I am more acceptable when known to be

married and expecting our first at that very minute. Yes. So
so. Cant complain musnt bla. My toe moves up and down to
the music. Course I want a dance. Feet still fast as fuck —
sorry. The girl dancing to me asks how I am doing and how
it feels to be a daddy shortly and I wink. I wink. Jesus
Christ. But she is there to make me enjoy being.
Understands all. I see it. Mother Earth. Someone's wife.
Frank's wife. The old mate Frank. I spot him seated and
chatting to a young thing, I followed my partner's eyes. And
I cannot be bothered at all. Everyone on the floor jumping
up and down but me now, and some other girl, half hoping
by the look of it. But I'm useless, useless. I just want to be in
this comfy chair wallowing and possibly getting to a stupor.

Someone at my elbow poking me to join in, Annie, wife
of old mate Frank, tugging on my arm: Come on —
expecting a song from you in a minute.

Jesus. I hear Big John singing the Green Grass of Home
and everybody silent. The old hometown looks the same.
Yes John. Give it laldy. The Big John fellow giving it big
licks. Yes John go on my son. And I am on my feet and into
the chorus with him. And when we finish they call for
another from me and a round of applause when I get on my
feet again. Just a minute: I say, Back in a flash. Desperately
needing a Jack Dash.

Quietly I close the door. Out and along the road. Up
Kelvin Way over the fence into the park. Soft crunch on the
low gravel path by the river. At the first tree everything
erupts. Retching for ages almost dozing on my feet there
vomit I know caking my shoes and trouser bottoms.
Staggering along. On the hill lying side by side three
wineys, males and a female sharing the bottle, talking; their
voices carrying in the night still. Asked for a smoke by a
single man on a bench and I give him one which I have to
light; his hands dirt lined, warm to the touch. He inhales
deeply: Stick with me big yin. I'll get us a few bob
tomorrow.

Water from the well near the gates. With difficulty I
manage over the jagged iron spikes.

Black coffee. Television late movie. Aware of the
surroundings here I am very aware, myself here, Jesus.
Sheets kicked down over my feet in the smelly bed. Yet not
the reeling brain, thanks to vomit. Good old vomit clears
heads. Is my momma and poppa. Too late to go downstairs
and find out from the neighbour if I am a daddy. She would
have slipped a note through my door anyway. Feet freezing.

Lumpen balls. I am stretching beneath this sheet pushing
my legs down my shoulders back as far as they all can go.

I shall be awake all night.

Once dressed I dip my head into the basin of cold
water. And again. Opening my eyes under water pulling
the skin back on the sockets so the water will enter my brain
and that.

Down and out the front close sprinting along the street
watching for a taxi as I go and in luck. Yes. Minutes later I
am knocking the door and explaining about the lack of
cigarette machines in the district so my apologies but I'll be
begging smokes for the rest of the night. Apparently I am
very pale. I tell Frank in a whisper I have been spending the
past while spewing the ring and that.

Thought so: He says. But they'll still get you to sing.

He poured me some beer and went to sit by his wife. I
remember Annie. All around now everybody seated in
couples with the music controlled.

Soon's I leave the dancing and singing stops. Eh: I
shout: What's the story here at all.

Aw Jesus Christ look who's back: Says Big John with a
laugh. Annie's cousin I think or maybe he is Frank's.

Someone takes records off and puts others on and slips
off her shoes. A couple of girls get up dragging their men
behind. The dancing resumes. Later on I sit beside the girl I
was mainly dancing with, Sue. I vaguely know her from
somewhere. Then the dancing halts and the bottle is
spinning for the first song, everyone glass in hand enjoying
themselves. When my turn comes Sue rises and leaves the
room. She stays away even after I have finished.

The old house is still standing.

At intervals I start awake and refill my glass if
necessary. Snuggling close in on the floor a couple barely
moving just rocking back and forth in this dim red lighting.
Nobody singing. Frank and Annie, Big John and his wife
chat with me for a few minutes about life in general and
why Moira and me dont appear these days. Possibly
relieved when I decide it is time I was going home. Sue
steps in front of me as I return from the bathroom. I think I
dozed off on the lavatory seat. I have to go ben see her
things or something more records maybe, well okay. I still
have a drink in my hand. And beside her on the bed
thumbing through the elpees and the forty fives showing I
am interested in who they are and the songs they sing. Also
some photographs. Big John is in the room saying Hullo

hullo hullo. Yes John how's tricks. Fine and that and you
Sue. Hullo John. Back out he goes. The lassie's cousin Big
John. I never knew that. And her big sister Annie and big
brother-in-law Frank my mate into the bargain and this wee
sister is browned off as well I know with all the play of the
front room and kitchenette with men and their wives and
the back and forth repartee and the rest of it wishing she
wasnt whatever age she is or married or engaged or even
winching steady or. And she is leading me on not knowing
what she is doing probably or maybe she does if she is at
least eighteen or nineteen or seventeen or fifteen for fuck
sake but she cant be or Big John would have spoken which
he still will do if I go fill my glass .Good looking lassie Sue.
Not bad yourself. Bit young but. Not so young as you think.
Aye. Easier to kiss through in the front with all of them there
like she says I did but here. And she is wondering what's up
and the door opens and in comes Frank after a pause as Sue
breaks off to lean down play a different record. O, says the
embarrassed big brother-in-law and mate Frank. I thought
you were away home man. At the same time backing out
the door to my smile and Sue's laugh as it closes over on us.
Under orders from Annie; I tell Sue. They probably think we
go to the naughty games ben here Aye; A smile. Well.
How's it going Sue. The married man I am shoves the hand
under her skirt and upwards without thought forgetting I
dont know her intimate at all between the thighs where her
warmth begins and all she does is smile a bit Jesus Christ
Sue and I am to take her now screw her I am supposed to
with no lock on the door and everybody in the front knowing
what's what and Annie most likely egging on her man to
come through throw me out etcetera and Sue lying back
and so making those thighs spread a little for me Christ Sue
while she is humming with the song? Her skirt up fankled
and wait I have to bar the door surely. I have to. I have to
bar it. She waiting there look. Not moved an inch nor said a
word but the smile still with closed eyelids and me the
pretend the chair will hold the door yet does it open in or
out the way for Christ sake back by her side and the
realisation but hot too hot and the shakes nervous hands
and knees twitching I with effort make contact lips to lips
touching no other part of her body I see rising to meet me
but I dont but kiss deep and stroking her hair at the nape
taking my weight on the left elbow for ages as if perhaps to
make up for the first direct thing I did too early I think yet
maybe it was right if I meant to be seducing though Jesus it

was habit only. And now this kissing on its own too much for me and increasing the twitching me the randiness uncontrolled and the knowledge of in the front room and all me of before tomorrow and the wife and that and the thought itself gone now Sue not a movement and Christ sake if she moved I could do but no I am to act on my own the bad bastard I will be less sense or I could see any.

Who's there, says Sue sitting up placing her hand on my thigh. Me, calls her big sister Annie. We're just listening to the records, says Sue and moving her hand along my thigh where the warmth. Alright, says Annie, but will I bring the sandwiches through or what? Are you making them, says Sue. Yes, says Annie, what kind do you want? What kind are you doing; and as she speaks this last Sue's hand is smoothing onto my balls outlining my hardon there between thumb and index finger. Gammon and cheese. Gammon for me. What about ... And Annie hesitates not saying my name. Gammon, says Sue. Yes gammon's fine. Okay then, from Annie. And are you making tea or coffee, asks Sue slowly as she is unzipping the fly enjoying her sister and me so much when Annie answers the young sister has the hand inside my pants pulling out my cock setting it alight all the time staring at the door question on question so her sister will stay there and I have to put my hand over her's for reasons and Annie goes for supper. Stretching fully back on the bed Sue laughing to herself and not to me exactly as I realise it is she lying not doing and me in the know means I have problems in carrying on where I left off earlier which has to be the case I know. Hand to her breast which she likes though hard to say, Yes Sue, I tell her, I know you. Nobody'll come in. You cant know that for sure. But she says nothing. You cant know for a certainty. She shrugs, It's okay. But I have lost it and considering a smoke and fresh drink right now she sits up changes the record, says she likes this certain one coming on leaning her head on my arm at the shoulder her hand on my chest like the pictures and even tickles my ear so okay. Okay. My fly is zipped now I spread her down on the bed again the way she was and. Just close your eyes Sue. I take her tights down so far and the same with the pants in maybe a professional slow way to get her going and that again though she maybe hasnt left off at all just me taking that for granted because it is so with me and the blouse out from the skirtband and unbuttoned lifting the bra over her breasts and catching the nipple between teeth and tongue and my fingers inside her stroking and down down using my mouth when Annie comes back along with the food perhaps and knocks the door with young sister Sue arms downwards hands holding my head there and so nothing unable to move less I take myself from her and I have to do that Sue sitting up chatting to big sister and now nude and getting the trousers down and playing with my hard hard thing all the time asking the questions and as Annie is answering this one Sue has moved her mouth forward clinging along to the tip with me there back lying out the game on the bed there and no not able to move at all knowing that door can open right now with Annie bursting straight in on wee sister Sue there doing me and me not moving but a muscle if the whole front room wife wean and in-laws all jump in together no I'll still be lying here out the game with Sue and me and her mouth and all of it Christ I'm finished Sue because of you and me.